Unconditional Love

Laura Barrett

Unconditional Love

An empowering guide to accepting your child's diagnosis, managing long hospital stays and building your new self

Written by Laura Barrett

COPYRIGHT

Copyright © 2022 by Laura Barrett

First Printing, 2022

ISBN 978-1-3999-1545-8

DEDICATION

To my husband Kev and my three boys Harry, Mylo and Bailey, thank you for enabling me to grow into the woman I have become through our life adventures together and bringing me so much joy and happiness.

In the borrowed words of Sir Elton John, my darling Bailey, I hope you don't mind that I put down in words, how wonderful life is now you're in the world.

Image credit: Kay Young Photography

CHAPTERS

The Story

The Support Guides

INTRODUCTION

I'm still unsure if this story is mine to share.

I'm not sure if it belongs to me, but rather to my youngest son, Bailey. Although the story involves me and has impacted me immeasurably, perhaps it is his story to tell? Or does the story begin with me, and then I hand over the baton and he tells it from his perspective when he is old enough, if he even so wishes, becoming the hero of his own life circumstance? I pray that I am making the right decision in sharing so openly and honestly, raw and from the heart, of our story. Perhaps that's it; it is *our* story.

Although this story begins as one of disbelief, upset and trauma, please know I write not as a victim, but as someone who went to the bottom of existence and made it out again stronger, happier, more empathetic and with a zest to live life to the max.

I have often wondered why I felt compelled to share our story, asking myself what value am I adding to anyone's life? My purpose is to offer hope and inspiration to all parents of a child with anything perfectly imperfect. Those special little Elmer elephants with a unique start in this world and journey through life. I am not writing to dwell. I share as a mother who wants to guide, support and comfort other families on a level of complete honesty, understanding and empathy.

I once heard that you should never share your painful experiences while you are in the moment suffering raw heartache, but rather journal and share those moments once your wounds have healed. Almost four years on, my wounds have scabbed over and are evolving into scars, and I am ready to share.

Thankfully, my older sister bought me a notebook and pen shortly into the start of this journey, and I scribed every single day for the first three months of this story. Of course, my journal is now invaluable in writing this book, which features several extracts directly from my diary. But at the time it was also the most perfect gift to articulate my emotions and to help make sense of it all.

So my first tip to any parent going through such adversity, is to journal. Write down your deepest, darkest, saddest thoughts and feelings, without judgement, just for you. Don't worry about whether you'll ever share it – I never thought I would. It's solely for you. Even if once you have healed, you burn it or tuck it under your bed or in the back of a drawer.

If you'd rather skip the story and go straight to the support guides, then please do. There you will find advice on so many learnings I gained through our journey of a life-changing diagnosis and long hospital admission.

Whatever you are going through with your little baby, I hope you find some value that makes your experience just that tiny bit more manageable.

This book is not just for those parents of children with cystic fibrosis, but for parents of any child with a challenging start who find themselves watching on, helplessly, and struggling to adjust to their new way of life. I speak to you, and your family and your children. I hear you, I feel you, and I hope you find comfort in knowing that your feelings are right, free and without judgement. They are yours, and your journey is yours. Just like this journey is mine ... [1]

---

[1] Please note, all specialist and hospital staff names in this book have been changed to protect their privacy.

THE STORY

From Hospital, to Home, to Hope

HOSPITAL

13th June 2018

Yesterday was our eight-year wedding anniversary, and to celebrate we brought home our third son, Bailey.

Born on 10th June, our older two boys Harry and Mylo were still at school, so there was a rare calmness to the house when my husband Kev and I arrived carrying our new bundle of joy. My mum had been looking after our older boys while we were at the hospital, and she had done the magical mum thing of changing my bedding and baking some cakes. It was the best welcome home gift in the world.

Soon enough the bigger boys were racing home from school to hold their new baby brother in our bed, watching on the iPad with him in their arms, while snuggled up next to me. It was the most perfect moment and one I will treasure forever. One where I was just me, with three sons and complete contentment. A rare moment I had before things changed forever. A day when all I had to worry about was the boys' dinner time, breastfeeding, tomorrow's clean school clothes and replying to friends' lovely messages of congratulations.

However, that was yesterday's memorable moment. Today there have been more poignant moments that will never leave my memory bank. My mum was still baking in the kitchen so we could ply tomorrow's guests with sweet treats and tea while they cooed over Bailey. Meanwhile, my husband Kev was lying on the chair with Bailey on his chest, sleeping so beautifully. It was something he had done with the other two boys too, and it felt so perfect seeing him enjoy those tiny first days with our one last child. As his muscular chest raised and lowered, Bailey seemed to be comforted by the subtle movements and breath.

In the afternoon, the big boys again scurried home, ran up to Bailey and me on our bed, showering him with drawings of elephants with his name on while clambering in for cuddles once more. Seeing them all in my bed, all my own creations, was and still is the most special moment of being a mummy.

Of course, as with all child-related moments, they only last seconds before someone is fussing, and soon enough Mylo was in tears for accidentally hitting Bailey on the head with his carrot, with Bailey's cries closely following at the shock, and before you knew it that moment was nothing but another memory logged in my brain. But this vivid, picture-perfect memory is something that would see me through some of my hardest days – a moment I would hold on to and recall when I needed it.

As I lay down to enjoy my second night in my own home as a family of five, I felt thankful for my newly made bed of fresh, crisp white linen. Little did I know this was the last night I would sleep in this bed before my life took a sharp turn.

14ᵗʰ June: home
The normal morning pre-school chaos and breakfast mayhem of a house of five ensued. As predicted, my night with Bailey involved very little sleep and a lot of feeding, winding and cuddling, but such is the life of a mum with a newborn.

Thankfully I still had both Kev and my mum on hand, so I simply lay in bed with a cup of tea listening to the pandemonium downstairs. Rushed kisses goodbye and a door slam later, and the house was quiet again. A relief spread over my body that I now had a full six hours of just caring for a newborn who couldn't move, talk or moan.

Yet to this day I still wish I had kissed Harry and Mylo once more that morning and held them for that little bit longer – not let them slip from my arms until I held just enough hug in me to last a couple of weeks at least. However, I didn't, so off they went with a hop and skip as Kev trotted them up to school, just around the corner from our house. It's a mere few minutes to walk there and back, yet in such a small time frame so much changed.

While Kev was gone, I tiptoed tentatively towards the shower. My caesarean section scar was still covered and sore, and consequently I couldn't stand up straight. Still, I wanted a wash, so I got undressed in the style of a one-hundred-year-old lady, unable to reach my feet or lift my arms.

That shower never happened. I never stepped into that shower that day. Instead, I saw green sick all over my bra and froze.

Naively, this actually wouldn't have concerned me if it hadn't been for a conversation with my midwife-qualified mummy just an hour or so earlier.

"Can you see this, Laura?" Mum said, pointing to a mark on Bailey's muslin.

"Yes, he was sick in the night – I think I fed him when really I should've winded him," I said, trying to justify my error of overfeeding my son. Surely being a mum third time round was meant to put me in better stead?

"No, look. It's slightly green. Can you see? I think it looks green," my mum said. At this point I knew her well enough to know she was trying to remain calm and levelled, relying on her forty years of midwife experience, but feeling her maternal emotions coming to the fore.

I will stand true to what I said in this moment. This moment when you would be forgiven for believing that my maternal instinct should have kicked in; something in me that simply knew there was something. Yet there was nothing. I felt nothing.

"I really don't think it looks green, Mum. Is it not just that colour because of the colostrum?"

That was it. My mum respected my opinion, said we would keep an eye on it and no more was said.

Until I was stood naked in the shower room, screaming for her to come in and examine the evidently green-tinged stains smothering my white nursing bra worn last night.

Mum stuck her head around the door and I started to cry – not because I thought even then that anything was wrong, but because I could see my mum's expression. I dreaded the tell-tale signs I could see across her face, which had become so familiar over the past thirty-six years of loving her.

She helped me get dressed and I went back to the bedroom, and soon Kev was home.

My mum had stayed with us when we had our two older boys and I always noted how respectful she was of giving Kev and I space to be a married couple even when she was staying with us – a chance to chat one-to-one and forge our own way. And again, I found her discreetly leaving our bedroom while I talked things through with Kev.

I actually have so many vivid memories of this time, but oddly I simply can't remember how I told him about my mum's concerns, the green, sick-covered bra and what we should do. Yet I do remember what he said, and I will thank him every day, until death us do part, for his levelled response.

"If there is even a chance there could be something wrong, then what are we waiting for? Let's go and get it checked."

Again, I hold my multi-tasking mummy hands up and will still admit, I actually was tempted not to take Bailey to hospital, but rather wait and see how the day went and if the green-tinge vomit cleared. I suggested as such as to Kev, but he simply wasn't having it. To see my husband, who is of calm, easy-going disposition, so strongly opinionated, made me feel a contrast of safe that he was by my side, but also worried that he was suddenly so assertive.

With that, we left. Kev carried Bailey, I hobbled along behind and Mum grabbed my still-unpacked hospital bag from Bailey's birth. She doesn't even know what possessed her to pick it up. It was an eyes-hand reaction. It was just lying there, half open, almost in the way. If she ever thought that we would actually *need* it, I don't know.

If I was looking for silver linings, my mum staying with us and noticing the green-hued vomit, Kev's rare opinionated decision making and mum picking up my bag are some of them.

14ᵗʰ June: Hospital
We pulled into the hospital car park, the same hospital we had left less than 48 hours previously following Bailey's delivery. However, that day we had left with happy faces from the maternity unit; today we arrived with concerned faces at the A&E department.

As we walked nervously into the reception area, it all suddenly felt very real and frightening.

Yet I still truly believed that we were wasting their time; that they would give Bailey the once over and send us on our way. Then I would be able to message my friends who I had just cancelled and tell them we were back home and they can pop over for cuddles and cake as previously planned.

Again, thanks to my mum's knowledge, she had prepped us as to what to expect when we arrived at the hospital.

"I need you to know what will happen when we get there. They will take Bailey from you, you won't be able to breastfeed and they will run lots of tests and prod and poke him," she advised, trying to keep her medical head intact.

That is exactly what happened. To the letter. Despite her warnings, it still caught me off guard.

Our bottoms had barely touched the cold, plastic waiting room seats before we were ushered in to the neonatal section and seen immediately.

Here, the doctors took control and ran all manner of tests and X-rays to see what, if anything, was wrong. I remember having to place Bailey on the hospital bed; this tiny two-day-old, perfect-looking baby, and he looked so small in that huge children's bed.

I still could hardly walk, so when the X-rays returned it was Kev and Mum who followed the doctor to the light box. Instead, I stayed by my little baby's bedside, using the hospital's breast pump to express my overfull, milky boobs.

The three of them came back towards the bed, and snuck around the privacy curtain with concerned looks. The doctor spoke, calmly and sympathetically, yet to the point.

"Laura, Bailey has a blockage in his bowel. This is causing the green sick and distended tummy. We need to remove it, but we cannot do it here. I am able to get you a bed at Great Ormond Street Hospital (GOSH) in London. We can take you there by ambulance now."

When people speak of an out-of-body experience, like you're not really there but looking at yourself, this is where it started.

I didn't know what to take in first. It seemed it was quite a serious problem. It seemed I wouldn't be going home tonight. And it appeared he had a distended tummy, of which I had not realised at all. Had I really already had two children? Had I really got all this so wrong? I felt so confused, and with that confusion a part of me drifted out, and hung in the air looking down on this frail, vulnerable woman sobbing as she held the tiny hand of her new baby.

14th June: In the ambulance

When shocking things happen in movies, they never really seem to deal with the practicalities of life. The logistics of the moment, as it were.

I say this because in this moment where we were meant to be flying through London in an ambulance and not going home any time soon, the three of us had to sort out the realities of it all.

Mum had to go home as she had to collect Harry and Mylo from school. Kev would have to take our car home as there wasn't anywhere to park at Great Ormond Street Hospital, and because we didn't know how long we would be, a carpark wasn't an option. Kev would then have to get the train from home to central London, where he would meet Bailey and me as soon as his speedy legs could take him.

So that was it; plan sorted. All of this clear-thinking in such a confusing time was nothing short of a work of genius. Two geniuses; Kev and Mum. I just sat there holding the baby, agreeing through my tears.

I walked with the nurses to the ambulance, which was the first time I was alone without mum and Kev, and I didn't utter a word for the shock and disbelief that was engulfing me. I could almost see myself from afar; I was me, looking in on me, watching it all unfold.

The ambulance driver told me that we were going to travel with the sirens on, but not to worry as it wasn't an emergency, it was just because we were hitting early rush-hour traffic in London. This high-pitched sound just added to the intensity of the moment and the disbelief I was experiencing. I couldn't quite compute all that was happening.

I lay down on the bed in the ambulance, holding Bailey the whole time. My C-section wound was already hurting and I was so uncomfortable, but I just carried on staring out of the small, rectangular-shaped window. I refused to look at the two ladies in the back with me, not because they weren't nice, but because I literally couldn't muster a word of conversation. They tried to talk to me, and were being so kind and gentle, but I wanted to be left alone with my whirring thoughts.

"Would you like me to hold the baby? You look like you're in pain," one lady asked.

I held on to Bailey even tighter, adamant I was not in pain and determined to be the one to hold my child all the way. My stitches were throbbing, but the pain in my heart was stronger, so I carried on holding Bailey, barely responding to the poor, kind nurse.

I am so grateful I endured the discomfort, as that was the last time I held Bailey freely, without some sort of tube coming from him, for a very long time.

14th June: Great Ormond Street Hospital

The ambulance crew lowered the bed out of the vehicle with me on it while holding Bailey, as they were concerned I wouldn't be able to walk all the way to his ward.

As they wheeled me in, it all looked so daunting and clinical. Eventually we reached Chameleon Ward, a place where I would soon know every crevice, detail, sound and face.

We were wheeled into the High Dependency Unit (HDU), a large room with six cots in it, separated by optional cloth curtains. They stopped the bed at an empty cot, where a tall, lean doctor stood waiting. He gently asked me to put Bailey onto the little bed they had prepared for his arrival.

Fear and overwhelm built up within me, while tears overflowed and rolled down my cheeks.

"I can't stand up while holding him. You'll have to do it," I said with my voice quivering and speaking so quietly I wasn't sure he could hear. With that, Bailey was taken from my arms. I wanted to grab him back. I wanted to go back to the time in the ambulance when I had him next to my chest. Yet I couldn't. By handing him over, I relinquished all control of my newborn baby.

The speed at which the doctors and nurses worked on Bailey made me feel even more worried. They were gentle, but worked with urgency, putting up drips, taking temperatures, writing down information, ordering tests. Meanwhile, I just sat there, numb.

I stared at Bailey, at the floor, at the cupboard next to his bed, at the black TV screen wondering why on earth I would watch anything. I've no doubt that I looked like a rabbit in headlights when I arrived that evening (and for a long time after). I felt like wherever I stood or sat, I was in the way and like I was in a goldfish bowl with everyone looking at me.

The mother in the bay next to me had two little pink twins snuggled up next to each other, one clearly a patient while the other was keeping her sister company. It was the most beautiful sight.

The lady in the bed opposite was smiling. I will never forget looking at her wondering how on earth she could be in there and smile. It seemed so indecent. So inappropriate. Why was she smiling? What on earth was there to smile about in here?

Doctors came and doctors went. Observations were done repeatedly. Cannulas were fitted and an IV drip put up. I don't even recall if I asked any questions. I was just vacant. Empty. Hollow. Torn. Petrified.

Kev finally arrived, for which I was so grateful for the comfort. He had clearly rushed as he was flustered and out of breath. How he sat on a train wondering what on earth was going on I'll never know.

The doctors confirmed that the blockage was being caused by stuck meconium. We watched with baited breath as they inserted a small tube into Bailey's bottom to try to dissolve and loosen it. Try as they might, they could not successfully dislodge or remove any of the thick, black, gooey baby poo.

It was clear we weren't going anywhere that night, so they very kindly said we could take one of the empty rooms on the ward and sleep there. I was so thankful we didn't have to be far from Bailey, but sleeping without your newborn just felt so wrong to me.

Bailey was now nil by mouth, so Mum had advised I keep expressing every three hours to keep my milk supply up for when Bailey could feed again. It was now midnight, so this meant I had to set my alarm for 3am in order to express. Just like a newborn wakes in the night to feed, I literally had to re-enact this manually with the breast pump to ensure my milk didn't dry up. My alarm went off, and Kev duly woke and helped me out of the bed and passed me the pump. I sat there staring at my milk flowing into the storage bottles. Once done, I had to take it to the nurses so they could freeze it for me so that it didn't go off.

I slowly made my way up the softly-lit, still corridor, and hovered around looking for a nurse on her night shift. I caught someone's eye and while handing over the bottles I asked, "Am I allowed to look in on Bailey, please?" My newborn should be at my side. I should be feeding him. I should be awake in the night because of him. Yet here I was, asking permission to see him because I wasn't sure I was allowed.

The nurse welcomed me in and said I could stay as long as I wished. I stood looking over Bailey, sleeping, dreaming I hoped, and I just sobbed. The sob that is so gut-wrenching it hurts your insides, but keeping the sound in so nobody saw my collapse. Tired, sore, emotionally wrecked, frightened, hormonal and away from my other two boys, I just went to pieces. Bailey looked so tiny, so vulnerable and so utterly perfect – how could there possibly be anything wrong?

15th June: Morning

My day began expressing milk and sitting by Bailey's bedside – a scene that would soon become all too familiar for far too long.

I hadn't eaten at all, but soon Kev appeared with tea and toast from the ward kitchenette, adamant I must eat. Although he was absolutely delighted at the free food and beverages on offer, I have never felt so sick by force-feeding myself. I knew I had to eat to keep my milk supply up, and if it wasn't for this I wouldn't have consumed a morsel.

Expressing my milk and focusing on being able to feed Bailey again became a fixation. It was the only thing I could control – if I did all I could to keep my milk ready, then he would soon be fed by me again and I would be fulfilling some sort of role as his mum. Control or nature, call it what you will, but it gave me something to aim for.

Kev and I just sat there, dumbstruck. No conversation. Just waiting for someone to come and tell us what was going to happen next. The doctor appeared and we stood to attention with anticipation. They told us they were going to perform a flush on Bailey, involving inserting a solution that should dissolve the blocked meconium to help him pass it out and release the blockage.

I felt a sense of relief swim over my body as this didn't sound too drastic, and if it worked, we might be able to go home. However, his exiting question soon drew short that sensation of relief.

"Is there a history of cystic fibrosis in your family, Mum and Dad?"

Maybe this was it. Maybe this was the point at which everything changed, yet I still don't think it was for me. Possibly for Kev, who replied, "Yes, my cousin in Ireland has it."

That exact point is definitely where everything changed from the doctors' perspectives. They clung to it like glue – like bees around a honey pot – and they never let the notion of our son having cystic fibrosis (CF) stray far from our minds.

Kev is of Irish decent, his wonderful parents both being Irish, yet he was born here in the UK. We had been to Ireland several times during our twenty-year relationship, and I had even met his cousin, but nobody really ever spoke of her CF. I didn't know what it was, what it entailed, or that it was even hereditary.

In contrast, I didn't know anyone in my family who had CF. I checked with my mum and she dug around, asking a few relatives in Australia if they knew of anything, but each time she drew a blank.

This was such a relief, because cystic fibrosis is a recessive genetic condition. This means that both parents must carry the faulty CF gene as the child needs to pick up both the genes from each parent in order to have the life-limiting condition. If they pick up one healthy gene but one faulty CF gene, the healthy one is the dominant and will override the recessive CF gene, making them a carrier but not symptomatic of the condition.

I knew nothing about genes, dominate or recessive, but I was on an express schooling programme where every single day my medical knowledge grew tenfold.

I had been a mother to two boys for six years and I hadn't done one first aid course. I knew nothing except how to put on a plaster and when I should likely run them to A&E, like when my eldest swallowed a pound coin and the other slit his wrist so deep it didn't even bleed. I'm squeamish, I don't take paracetamol even when I have a throbbing headache and I had never spent a night in hospital other than to give birth to the boys. But crikey, was I learning on the job.

So as far as I understood, for as long as nobody knew of cystic fibrosis on my side of the family, it was not the cause of Bailey's blocked bowel. He couldn't possibly have CF if my family didn't carry the gene, which is what we understand to be the case. This only left the potential of an anatomical cause that they could hopefully fix with surgery. Not ideal, but definitely the better outcome.

"Laura, there's only around a five percent chance that this isn't cystic fibrosis," pleaded Kev, with an acceptance of a potential diagnosis.

Now to say that my husband and I handled this whole situation differently and how we coped with it, is an understatement. Since our arrival Kev had been researching (AKA Googling) everything – the person who funded the Chameleon ward, the consultant's career history and of course every fact and stat about cystic fibrosis.

I on the other hand, hadn't been online since we left home two days ago. I couldn't check anything online as I was more petrified than I have ever been in my life. I had to deal with the facts as they were presented to me by the specialists working on my individual child, and not have any other noise or fearmongering in my head.

For some, this difference would cause friction, and for some it gives balance. We were at either end of the spectrum in the way we dealt with each event and each day, but we respected each other's way and allowed ourselves to find our own way in our own time. Our marriage did not falter. We did not grow stronger. We did not grow weaker. We didn't blame nor question. We were the constant in our ever-evolving storm.

Of course I knew Kev had clearly Googled this five percent stat on his phone, as how on earth would he pull that out of his head?

Although I respected his desire to be informed, I clearly and firmly responded, "Then we are in that five percent Kev, because we don't have it on my side of the family. None of my family have the CF gene, so even if you carry the gene, I don't, so we are in that 5%. I'm telling you. I just know it."

Whether it was truly my belief, or a strong survival tactic, I'll never know, but I was vehemently adamant. Just as I believed there was no need to take him into hospital in the first place, I now truly believed he did not have CF. I would have put my life on it. There was nobody in my family with it, so that ruled it out. I just wasn't of sound mind enough to think straight and realise that I had been wrong just the day before.

15th June: Afternoon

They wanted to do a flush on Bailey in the hope this would dissolve the stuck meconium. For them to perform this procedure we had to go down to X-ray. Kev chose to be next to Bailey during the flush as I still couldn't stand without pain, so I had a seat behind the plastic window instead. I looked at Kev with his special X-ray coat and his worried expression, and I saw Bailey so tiny, naked and cold, and I started crying.

I still couldn't believe or accept that we were here or that this was happening.

As we waited, I could see Bailey's internal organs on the screen. I squinted my red-raw eyes in the hope I might suddenly become some medical whizz that could miraculously make my child better, or identify something the doctors hadn't, but alas, no.

I had the screen in my vision and I followed that flush with my eyes. The flush is designed to show any blockage or narrowing, and also dissolve the stuck meconium. I tried to use the power of my eyes to clear the flush; to help the solution push through the blockage. It was taking far longer than they said it would and soon the first doctor explained he couldn't get through the blockage. Someone more senior arrived, and after another very long attempt, they got there.

Today was also the day my sister finally got to meet her third and youngest nephew. I didn't know how to handle the whole visitor situation. Mum had been liaising with my sister Jules this whole time, and she said that Jules wanted to come and see us as she was out of her mind with worry. Of course I wanted to see her, but part of me wondered if it was appropriate (would the doctors think I was just treating it like some social event?), and part of me kept thinking that we would be home soon and I would far rather see people in the comfort of my own lounge.

It was becoming clear that we weren't going anywhere any time soon as the nurses kept saying about longer term accommodation. I kept ignoring them and shuffling it to the back of my mind as I couldn't bear the thought of what this actually meant. I relented, and agreed for my sister to visit.

Unconditional Love

Kev and I walked alongside Bailey's cot as it was wheeled back from X-ray into his room, and as we entered I saw my sister's rouged face, walked over to her and we hugged and cried. My sister doesn't often cry, so this made me cry even more – it almost added to my fear, as it cemented how serious and desperate our situation clearly looked to an outsider.

Nobody ever envisaged that auntie Jules' first ever cuddle with Bailey would be to warm him up from the X-ray room, attached to a drip and with cannulas in both hands. It all felt so alien.

The doctors soon came by to say that there was no visible cause for the blockage and that it should soon start dissolving the meconium. I couldn't believe my ears. It sounded like this was going to clear and then we would be on our way home to our boys. This was it, job done. Nothing but a stuck poo. Definitely one to share with Bailey's friends at his twenty-first birthday party!

However, some meconium did pass, but not nearly enough.

The doctors kept returning and visibly grew increasingly worried that it wasn't working as well as hoped. Bailey's stomach was still very full and exceptionally distended, which was now even worse as the liquid from the flush had gone in, but was not coming out as it was meant to. With his tummy fuller than before, Bailey was now at serious risk of a perforated bowel.

Surgery was becoming more spoken about and more likely as the last resort to clear the stuck meconium and check for any potential internal anatomical issues that might be causing the blockage.

I was jolted by my phone buzzing on silent mode. It was a number I didn't recognise, so I answered it hesitantly.

"Laura, it's your midwife. I'm here for Bailey's day five heel prick test. I'm on your doorstep. Will you be home anytime soon as I can wait for a bit if you need?"

I stayed silent. I mean, what was I meant to say? This woman was calling to do the blood screening test for the very condition we might be in here for, and she was on my doorstep and I was in a top London children's hospital.

"I'm sorry, we aren't home," I replied. "We were taken to Great Ormond Street Hospital and they don't know when we will be home."

The poor woman, now I felt for her. She was speechless, and came out with some sort of confused response and a very kind offer of helping me once we get home. I hung up and returned to our current plight.

Today was the day Bailey was supposed to be born via a planned C section, but here he was just five days old, possibly about to undergo surgery. Our hearts were breaking. I began to wish he hadn't arrived early; that he was still warm and safe in my tummy, being fed by me via his umbilical cord. Then these people wouldn't be prodding and poking; he would just be blissfully floating around completely untouchable to the outside world. I longed not just to hold him, but to put him back in my tummy and keep him safe from all he had already been subjected to, and all the he was about to endure.

16th June

Today a new consultant entered our lives, and one I will remain eternally grateful to; Doctor Crosley. Doctor Emma Crosley; an Australian with a stellar career and two sons, according to Kev on Google. While I didn't feel the need for our son's surgeon's professional and personal break down, I did need to know the hard, raw facts of what we were looking at here.

One thing about me, I hate not knowing. The not knowing kills me. The limbo stage. I am the same in any situation, and this appeared to be no different. No matter how daunting, I have to know every single detail, and this was something that transpired throughout this journey.

Bailey's tummy was still hard and distended, and only the smallest amount of meconium had passed into his tiny, yet oversized nappy. Following another X-ray that continued to show a very full intestine, Dr Crosley was concerned that Bailey might suffer a perforated bowel.

"We will operate tomorrow."

Again, words that are startling, cutting and frightening.

Tomorrow would be Sunday. A day we would have been at home as a family of five with Harry and Mylo enjoying their new baby brother and showing him off at cricket on the common in our village. Oh, our village, our home, our boys. It all felt like another life.

I returned to the clinical, sterile world I had been transported to, and asked for as much information as humanly possible.

They would operate to fit a stoma, basically bringing part of Bailey's bowels outside to divert around the blocked bowel and alleviate his distended stomach. If they found anything anatomical which they could 'fix' while operating, then they would.

Unconditional Love

While we still had so many unanswered questions, I felt a sense of relief for knowing the next steps and strangely comforted by the fact some action was being taken. If they found an internal issue they could fix, that would be that – heal from the operation then homeward bound.

Kev's mum Mary and sister Clair also visited today. They both appeared calm, yet concerned. We chatted to Mary about her thoughts on the possibility of cystic fibrosis. She's always quite a reserved lady, finds the positives in most situations and very emotionally in control. Did she think it was CF? I just couldn't bring myself to ask.

"There but for the grace of God go I," she would say.

Religious people always call upon God when they need something. Usually when they're desperate. Few folks seldom call upon Him to celebrate, congratulate or thank Him. I know I am guilty of this.

Well, at the pit of our desperation, Kev and I found ourselves in the most beautiful Great Ormond Street Hospital chapel on our knees asking for God's help. We opened the large, solid wooden door to reveal an exquisite gold-gilded interior.

There was the most beautiful little tree adorned with an array of notes tied on – the pleas of desperate parents and family members begging, hoping, praying. I read a few, but I felt like I was reading someone's most personal diary. It felt hugely inappropriate, so I stopped.

We both wanted to write a little message in the hope God would hear us, take pity on us and bring our son back to good health and home to his family.

Dear Lord,
Please keep Bailey healthy and strong. Please let him come home to his brothers Harry and Mylo very soon. Please give him a happy, healthy life going forwards.
Amen x

Kev tied it to the tree, while tears streamed down my face like a river.

Kev doesn't cry. Ever. I mean, I have never seen that man cry in twenty years. In contrast, I cry at everything – a sad book, a happy film, seeing a friend after a long time or when I upset one of my boys.

So there I was, eyes streaming, son in a hospital bed upstairs awaiting an operation and he looked at me concerned. "What just happened? Why are you crying?"

Is he for real? Truly, why am I crying? No wonder they say men are from Venus and women are from Mars. We were in the same room, the same situation, but we could have been on different planets at that moment. However, I loved our alternate approaches and ways of coping. It frustrated me, but at a time when I never thought I would laugh again, he made me feel something. A tiny flicker. Sometimes even a smile. Even if I couldn't muster a laugh on the outside, I was silently laughing on the inside. Our different approaches would become a constant source of amusement and freshness throughout our journey.

I didn't want to be away from Bailey for too long, so we left the chapel. As we were heading back, Kev had heard of (read 'Googled') a garden in the hospital and wanted to visit it together. We clumsily found our way, asking for directions as we went, like we were in some oversized, luxurious hotel, and as he swung open the door it hit me; fresh air.

I hadn't set foot outside this place since we had come in several days ago. Like everyone in there, we had lived solely off recycled, air conditioned air. I breathed in lung fulls of London-standard fresh air and it felt so good. We sat on the bench in the most tranquil garden setting; exhausted, dumbfounded and bereft. We just sat there, but we sat there together, leaning on each other, taking a breath before we moved on to our next step in this journey.

17th June – Operation Day

I found myself staring in the mirror today and I just didn't recognise myself. Of course, my body looked different as I had just had a baby via C section only a week ago. But it was my face, I hardly looked like me. And my eyes – there was a painful sadness right at the core of them. It wasn't an emptiness, but more of a darkness.

Pity. I think that was it. I was looking back at the girl staring at me in the mirror and I felt sorry for her.

The individual rooms at GOSH consist of the baby's bed, a lay-back chair, a couple of white plastic chairs for guests, a TV that hangs on a hinged arm so you can move it around depending where you're sitting in the room, plus a private shower room. This is where I had found myself stuck staring at my reflection in the mirror. Each identical room has a full-length mirror in the wet room.

I had woken early, nervous about the day's events, so thought I would try to freshen up with a shower and a rare dose of clean clothes.

Unconditional Love

Doctor Crosley appeared and confirmed Bailey would go down about twelve noon providing there were no delays with her prior surgeries. Now sometimes in life, it's not what you know, but who you know. While Kev had been researching Bailey's soon-to-be surgeon online, which was now verging on stalking, I had a different approach. I have an exceptionally dear friend, Amy, who happens to be a surgeon, and knows a thing or two about this medical lark. I fired off a message almost asking her for a personal reference of Dr Emma Crosley, and what do you know, her reputation preceded her. Amy's message was clear and simple.

"The Legend."

Right then and there, Dr Crosley' title was born.

We had a legend operating on our son. The best surgeon this country had to offer, and we had bagged her for our special boy.

However, it appears that when One is a Legend, One comes with an entourage of specialists, registrars, doctors and nurses. Every time The Legend walked into Bailey's room, a sea of people would follow along behind. It sometimes felt like we should have pulled out the tea and cake and got the party started.

I desperately wanted to have a private word with Dr Crosley, one mother to another, and let her know that I knew how amazing she is at her job thanks to my friend Amy.

The Legend and her minions left the room, and I plucked up the courage to follow them out and catch her in the corridor.

"Dr Crosley, please may I have a quick word in private?"

I honesty felt sick. What on earth was I doing? Who was I to question a top London surgeon? Yet she obliged and stepped to one side to be alone with me. My heart was physically racing.

"I have a friend who is a surgeon. She tells me you're the very best. I need you to do your absolute best in there on our son. He has two big brothers waiting for him at home. I need him to get well and get him home. I know you have two sons too, and I just need you to do your absolute best."

Unfazed by the apparent investigative work into her personal life, she simply reassured me that it was a simple procedure and that Bailey wasn't even that small to be operating on. She was used to working with neonatal babies, so this six-pounder wasn't as tiny as he seemed to me.

Until this point, I hadn't taken any photos of Bailey while at GOSH. It felt inappropriate to do so – my child was not a freak show to be paraded, and I also worried about what the nurses would think. However, it dawned on me that if I didn't take any at all, his baby photo album would be empty for the first week or so of his life.

While no nurses were in the room, I quickly took a photo of Kev holding Bailey next to his cot, tubes and machines connected. No fluffy teddy, no cosy blanket, no skin to skin – just a clinical photo of Kev looking shattered and Bailey about to undergo an operation aged one week. Far from your perfect baby photo, but at least we would have something to show Bailey when he was older.

Minutes became hours and hours became days. We sat in the room watching the hands slowly tick around the clock face, too frightened to nip out in case someone came to collect Bailey for his procedure. Twelve o'clock had come and gone, and after two further hours of painstaking waiting, someone walked through the door.

"Dr Crosley is ready for Bailey now," the nurse said.

I suddenly came over all peculiar. I really didn't feel well all of a sudden. I know this sounds so awful, and I've not been the shining example of a mother thus far with multiple errors of judgement, but I couldn't go. I couldn't take our son to theatre. I couldn't bring myself to watch this tiny baby be anaesthetised and mauled over by an entire team of specialists. I just couldn't take any more.

Kev wanted to go, so he carried Bailey down with the nurse into the anaesthetic room and stayed with him until he lay there sleeping peacefully.

During the operation, we got some tea and sat in the gardens and prayed in the chapel. Basically just killed time. Kev fell asleep (again, I have no idea how one sleeps at such a time, but there we are) and I watched the clock while expressing yet more milk. It read 5pm, which meant Bailey had now been in for three hours. I frantically text Amy with nothing but fear in my words, asking for every piece of information she could offer. Her response was reassuring, saying he should be back soon, and true to her word, shortly after a nurse walked in.

"Bailey is in recovery and you can come down to pick him up now."

I moved off the chair probably the swiftest I had moved this entire time, and ran to be with Bailey, harbouring nothing but guilt that I had let him down a few hours earlier at a time when he needed me more than ever.

We saw Bailey in the recovery room and he looked content and alert, which wasn't what I had been expecting. He had been left with a stoma to the right side of his abdomen, and a small horizontal wound across the middle of his stomach, running just above his tummy button.

Dr Crosley came to talk to us. I found it strange to see her in her scrubs as she was always so beautifully presented when we saw her on the ward. She comforted us that all went well and she had created the stoma, and she confirmed there was no anatomical issue for the blocked bowel.

I found this such a hammer blow. Not of course because I wanted there to be anything wrong with our boy, but this would have potentially been an easier outcome than the continued possibility of cystic fibrosis.

They also took a biopsy from the bowel to test for Hirschsprung's disease, which is an abnormality to the bowel.

Dr Crosley confirmed that there was a large amount of meconium, which had clearly built up for quite some time, even while Bailey was in utero.

My mind started racing. It's as if I was joining the dots.

Bailey was born via C section at thirty-eight weeks due to reduced movement. Kev was in Spain for a rugby tournament, and I was on the south coast with Harry, Mylo and my dad. However, while we were there I had two episodes of reduced fetal movements, so I went to the local hospital to have my baby bump checked.

The first time was fine and they sent me on my way, but the second time, although they could hear a heartbeat and all appeared fine, the baby was showing no further signs of growth. Given this was my second visit, they advised I go back home and visit my usual hospital to get their advice.

Nothing about Bailey's entry into this world was simple it seems, as I then dashed back to our coastal flat, where Dad was on the beach with the boys. I frantically said I had to go immediately, so I took the boys and left him to pack up. On the way home I called my Mum and asked her to meet us at our house so she could have the boys while I went to hospital for checks. They knew I was coming as the other hospital had rung ahead.

Once there, they scanned me and all had appeared fine, but due to reduced movement they decided to bring forward my planned C-section. However, Kev was still in sunny Spain. I explained my situation to the nurse and said she would give him until tomorrow to fly home. We managed to get Kev on a plane from Spain to England the next day, and then he drove straight to the hospital to be at my side for our third son's arrival.

So as you can see, this whole third baby thing was anything but plain sailing so far.

19

The point is, I was scanned three times just before Bailey's arrival. If this meconium blockage had been building up for some time while Bailey was in my womb, why hadn't anyone seen it? Could something have been done differently if it had been spotted?

I shared all my questions and concerns with Dr Crosley, but in truth, none of it would have made a huge amount of difference. The events leading up to all this may have altered slightly, but the outcome would have been the same, and the real outcome of which was still unknown to us.

We lethargically wheeled Bailey back to HDU for frequent post-op monitoring, all the while I was feeling like all hope was lost. As we arrived, there she stood. Amy. My off-site medical advisor and mother-of-two herself. There wasn't a more perfect person to arrive at a more perfect moment.

Clearly she had sensed the utter desperation and panic in my messages, and had jumped on the train to be the dutiful friend and medic extraordinaire (and probably to catch a glimpse of The Legend).

I hugged her so tight I thought she might stop breathing – the gratitude and comfort in her arrival was so intense. At this time, Bailey was content and we managed to have a lovely chat over a hot cuppa. Yet shortly after Amy's departure things took a drastic down turn.

Bailey had been on a mix of paracetamol and morphine since his operation. They had to get the balance of them right; enough but not too much. Quite tricky I'd imagine when you have a patient that can't tell you if they're feeling pain or not. Just like mothers, they use the method of "if baby cries, he is likely in discomfort and needs more painkillers". However, they thought they had given Bailey too much morphine as his breathing kept stopping – like he was holding his breath.

Within what felt like seconds, there were about ten people crowded around Bailey's bed. I stepped out of their way, completely and utterly overwhelmed by what was evolving. They got Bailey an apnoea mat and the doctors administered a 'reversal' drug to reverse the effects of the morphine, but now it went too far the other way and Bailey was in excruciating pain from the surgery.

To this day, I have honestly never heard a baby scream in such a way. It was both gut wrenching and heart-breaking. I have never felt so totally and utterly helpless towards one of my children as I did in that moment. I could do nothing but stand and watch. Gormlessly stand there and watch as ten medical professionals of all specialities tried to help this child. Tried to achieve the optimum balance of comfort. And tried to regulate his breathing. I never went into the hospital fearing I would lose Bailey. That was never a real concern of mine because I felt that whatever the outcome someone would be able to do something, such the miracle is modern medicine. That moment though is when I feared we might lose our son. Not because of a blocked bowel, nor CF nor an infection. But because of the effects of morphine on our baby. I stood there watching, fearing the absolute worst thing a parent could fear. I stared, and I hoped and I prayed deep inside of me that all would be OK.

Eventually I walked up to his bedside, using my maternal rights as my passage through to our boy, and I comforted him the only way I could; I stroked his hair, I sung, I sssshhhhed and I held his teeny hand. So tiny and yet he had gone through more medically then I had done in my whole thirty-six years of life.

As the morphine dose gradually increased, Bailey settled and I calmed. But we were all exhausted from an exceptionally traumatic day. Kev and I reluctantly left Bailey's bedside at midnight and I returned at 5am the following day, with a 3am milk express session in between. You're not meant to sleep as a new mummy, anyway.

18th June

As I sat by Bailey's bedside in the early hours of the morning, expressing yet more milk, he looked at peace. I prayed he would remain oblivious to any of what was going on around him and that this stage wouldn't negatively impact his later development somehow.

I longed to hold Bailey in my arms, but there were so many tubes now that I felt nervous in case I caught one. The nurse helped lift Bailey carefully out of his cot and lay him in my arms. I just sat, me and him, stroking his hair and talking to him so he knew I was still ever present.

Soon Dr Crosley came to check Bailey and told us both that he was recovering well and could have two millilitres of milk every two hours. This was a significant step. Finally, we could get him back onto milk. Now, I appreciate it's only two millilitres, but it could have been two litres for the reaction I gave it.

I frantically expressed off some milk and used two one-millilitre syringes to slowly squeeze it into Bailey's mouth. He reminded me of a tiny little baby bird, sipping excitedly at the warm, milky liquid. The comfort I felt in his continued love for milk was met by the reality of a harsh cry when it ended. We weren't allowed to give any more than the amount stated, but Bailey clearly felt he was being short changed.

Slowly, the stoma started working and the stoma bag that covered it began to fill. It all just felt like such positives steps, and although we still didn't know the root cause of all this, I truly believed we were heading in the right direction at last.

Since we had arrived at GOSH, they had struggled to get enough blood from Bailey's tiny veins to run the genetic test for cystic fibrosis. So while he was asleep during his operation, they had inserted two cannulas; one in his hand and one in his foot. However, today the vein in his little foot collapsed, meaning that cannula could no longer be used. If the same thing happened to the one in his hand, we were back to square one.

The doctor started to discuss a PICC line with us (PICC being an abbreviation for Peripherally Inserted Central Catheter). I had never heard this term before, being the medical novice that I was, but in simple terms it's a longer line than a cannula that uses the big vein that carries blood into the heart. It's commonly used for longer-term intravenous (IV) medications and also to draw back blood for testing.

At this point it's fair to say my heart stopped as this sounded absolutely horrific, but the constant needles and cannula attempts were causing Bailey so much pain that I wondered if it would be a better option, albeit one that sounded like we were in here for a while yet.

We had now been at GOSH for five days, and not only had they not sent off bloods for genetic testing, they hadn't even decided how they were going to obtain enough blood to perform the test. Once submitted, the results for the genetic test take two to three weeks. It all just felt like such a long time, and I wasn't sure where this left us in terms of getting home.

Every day, one of the specialists would talk about CF and ask a few more questions. Every day, Kev did a bit more digging around while I stuck my head in the five percent cloud. We prayed daily that it wasn't the outcome, as did our entire family. Could you imagine if all this was simply an extreme form of constipation? All this just for a stuck poo? Now that would be a great ending.

The personal support we received from Great Ormond Street Hospital was second to none. Therapists would visit our room and offer the opportunity to talk about the trauma we had endured. I say trauma without hesitation, as this is exactly what it was.

On top of this, a lovely lady visited to help equip us with the tools and language to help explain to Harry and Mylo about Bailey's rather unsightly stoma. I didn't like the look of it, so I knew the boys would feel funny about it if Bailey was to go home with the stoma in place.

I remember one of the main things Mylo wanted to do was have a bath with Bailey; all three of them in a bubbly tub. So I wanted to find a way to explain and normalise this part of organ that was now on the wrong side of Bailey's body. She gave us a child's booklet about stomas and introduced us to Buttony Bear from the Breakaway Foundation; a little bear with a button on his tummy and a stoma bag over it. I ordered our fluffy friend online to help the boys, but also to help explain all this to Bailey when he was older.

19th June

Britain was having its hottest summer on record, set to stay that way for weeks, and we were missing it all, stuck in an air-conditioned hospital with windows that didn't open and offered a brick wall of another building for a view. It could've snowed and it wouldn't have caught my attention. The outside world didn't exist to me. There was no life beyond this hospital room.

Visitors came and went; they dressed in pretty summer tops and frocks, while I sported oversized knitted cardigans and leggings. I could barely be bothered to wash my hair and make-up wasn't even in my bag. Day by day, I was losing myself; who I was, all I knew. I just longed to go home to my boys. I yearned for them, daily.

Yet far from the central London streets of our current crisis, we had two other young sons back at home who needed taking care of. Although hard to mentally shift myself to real, everyday life, it perhaps saved my sanity a little while in this living nightmare.

Bailey had been born in June, also known to some as the rugby off season, which when your husband is a professional strength and conditioning coach for Premiership rugby club Saracens, is somewhat handy. The timing of Bailey's birth (plus those of Harry and Mylo who were also born late May and early June respectively) was one of our biggest blessings in this sorry saga, because it meant Kev could stay with us at GOSH, while my Mum could stay at home with the big boys.

Yet today, Kev was going back home for the first time since Bailey's arrival at hospital. I felt a little nervous, but it was just for the day and Mum was coming to be with me. I was delighted that the boys would finally have a parent home for them and a slight sense of normality.

While Kev was at home, I finally found the strength to speak to my darling big boys. I saw their little faces on FaceTime for the first time since all this began, and my heart welled. I wanted to reach through the phone and grab them into my embrace. I was so happy to see them, but it also made me want to get us home even more and made my heart physically ache.

Throughout the day we continued to give Bailey boy two millilitres of milk every two hours via a syringe. It was but a dribble, but felt like a lot.

The doctors were still very concerned that Bailey only had one remaining cannula, because if this went, then they couldn't give him his IV drip or painkiller. They explained that in order to get a PICC line done it would require another general anaesthetic. I felt a twinge of frustration they hadn't just done this when Bailey was in his previous operation, but I guess they had been trying to avoid it in the hope cannulas would suffice. On top of this, there was a waiting list for the PICC line procedure, and nobody was overly reassuring that the cannula would last until then.

Despite the one good cannula, they *still* had not obtained enough blood for the genetic test. Every time they tried, it either stopped bleeding or clotted before they had put it into the blood bottles.

A little light relief arrived in the form of my friend Hannah. She was on her way to meet her husband after work as they were going to an outdoor summer concert. She looked absolutely beautiful and I felt embarrassed at both my situation and my appearance. It was so lovely to see her, and although she looked visibly moved and emotional at what was presented before her, it was so wonderful to have some friendly company. We cooed over Bailey and drank the watery, but free, tea from the ward kitchenette. A far cry from summer music events, but I was so grateful for the distraction.

It was so calm while Hannah was with us, but as soon as she left the day took a somewhat unexpected turn, as Bailey's sole remaining cannula stopped working.

Just as before, his tiny vein had collapsed and he now wasn't getting his drip nor his painkillers, and they also stopped his milk too in case he needed another general anaesthetic for an emergency PICC line, for which you need to be nil by mouth a few hours prior.

Until they could sort this rather dire situation, they gave Bailey sucrose drops. I put it on my finger and let him suck it off; apparently this kept his blood glucose levels up. A nurse came along every so often and kept pin-pricking him to check his glucose levels weren't significantly dropping. It felt like they were always taking so much blood from him.

I began to feel that what helped one thing, hindered another; like it was a very fine game of balance, sadly with my child's wellbeing constantly at stake. Needles, cannulas, pin prick testing, PICC lines – I had become familiar to such an alien world so scarily quickly that I couldn't recall a life without these medical terms.

Bailey was put on the emergency list for a PICC line, and his slot was for 8pm that night. In the meantime, a specialist arrived with an ultrasound machine to try to find a useable vein for another cannula insertion. They agreed to try one in Bailey's other arm, and if this didn't work they would go ahead with the PICC as planned.

Kev and I walked away. Sometimes, when you are in these emotional and exhausting situations, you have to learn when to step back and protect what is left of you. Of course, like most parents I am sure, I wanted to hold Bailey's hand throughout. I wanted to take away his pain, the procedures and all of this and put it onto myself. But rationally I knew this wasn't humanly possible, so the only thing I could do was save the remains of my ruined being and try to survive and be strong for him. Neither of us fought to stay for the procedure, both exhausted from seeing our baby undergo yet another needle.

We returned to learn the cannula had worked and Bailey hadn't made a murmur thanks to those magical sucrose drops. Yet as soon as the specialist had left Bailey's bedside, he returned with an idea.

"If Bailey can stay that still with sucrose drops, how would you feel if we tried to do the PICC line using these, rather than putting him under another general anaesthetic?"

My heart was in my throat; it all sounded very dangerous, yet for some reason I liked the idea as it meant Bailey didn't need to endure another general anaesthetic. With that, we were signing yet another consent form.

20th June

At 9:15am the nurse came to collect Bailey for his PICC line procedure. I carried Bailey down, who had now exhausted himself so much that he fell asleep on the way. I entered the room and there was a large blow-up, heated pillow for him to lie on. As I placed down my sleeping son, he opened his eyes and we just stared at one another directly into each other's eyes. Today my sister and Dad were due to visit, which was the first time Bailey would meet his grandad. When we returned to the ward, my sister Jules and my dad were there. They were a welcome distraction from what was going on downstairs where Bailey lay.

Just forty-five minutes later, the nurse returned to inform us that the procedure had worked and Bailey had been so still they managed to get the PICC line done just using the sucrose drops. Way to go Bailey!

Kev and I collected Bailey and took him to his grandad for cuddles on his protruding tummy, just like he had done with all six of his grandchildren.

With the PICC line now in place, the nurse came and finally got the bloods required for the genetic test. As I watched Bailey's blood flow from his vein into the tubing, I realised this would finally determine if our son had cystic fibrosis. We were told the results would take about two weeks.

With so much going on the last few days, I had almost forgotten that I'd had abdominal surgery via C-section and had my own wound to take care of. When I checked Bailey's surgical wound I realised how much better it was healing compared to mine. Of course this was his young baby body working magic, but it also made me think that I'd perhaps better get checked given I hadn't seen a midwife or health visitor since Bailey's birth.

The nurse told me I could book an appointment with their on-site midwife. Honestly, this hospital had everything a mum could need in terms of support, both physical and mental. I was so impressed. I had an appointment booked in for that day, so I headed down to the right department.

While in the waiting room, I spied a familiar face. It was the lady from the cubicle next to us while on HDU – the lady with the twin girls.

"Hi, I'm Liana."

"Hi, I'm Laura. How is your little girl doing? They're twins aren't they?"

We chatted and Liana told me she was here for mastitis, poor thing. It made me feel sorry for us both that we were both trying to heal ourselves after giving birth and breastfeeding, all while dealing with so much for our little babies.

Liana told me all about her twin girls and how she was juggling her time between hospital and home. It was so lovely to meet her and I hoped we would bump into each other again on the ward soon.

Once I was back in our room with the confirmation my wound was healing fine, the doctors came by to say we could start giving Bailey milk again, starting at two millilitres but this time increasing by two millilitres for each two-hourly feed. Eventually we progressed from syringing it in, to feeding him with a bottle, which he drank beautifully. We had turned a corner, and things were looking up. I could see a little ray of light at last. That night Kev and I sat by Bailey's bed, and for the first time we put the TV on and just chilled out. As Bailey was on the HDU ward again, we had off-site accommodation, but luckily it was just over the road. We kissed our baby goodnight and headed off to bed.

This day had been the first good day since we arrived.

21st June

I woke early, feeling uneasy about being away from Bailey's bedside, so I left Kev in bed to sleep while I walked over to the hospital. As I stepped along the quiet morning London streets, it was the most gorgeous sunrise, plus it was my mother-in-law's birthday. I felt then like it was going to be a great day!

When I arrived I gave Bailey his bottled breastmilk, then expressed off some fresh. Kev soon arrived and we sat drinking tea and feeling positive.

My mum also visited, and I said she could give Bailey his next bottle, however it soon transpired she couldn't, as the doctor then told us that we could try timed breastfeeds. I felt so elated. All that expressing every three hours for the past seven days was about to pay off. My milk supply was fine, now all he had to do was latch.

Bailey's nose tube was removed, as was his drip, and for the first time in ages he was a free baby. Free from tubes, needles and drips. I was so happy my eyes began to well.

I held Bailey, freely at last, and snuggled him into my breast and that was it, he was away. He had remembered how to latch. Go Bailey!

They put Bailey back into his own room off HDU, because as I now had to stay in order to feed Bailey throughout the night. Kev had to go home to be with Harry and Mylo, so it was just my baby boy and me in our own little world of breastfeeding and snuggles, just how it should have been all along.

One week. Seven days. It's strange as a week isn't that long really, but so much has happened in that time that it felt like a lifetime. Think how little really happens in a week – the monotony of our daily and weekly routines.

And yet in one week our world had been turned upside down, but now it appeared to be starting to stand upright again.

22nd June

Today they let me breastfeed on demand. This was truly it now – we were on our way. I felt like I was back in control, following my innate maternal instincts, feeding Bailey as I wished.

Dr Crosley began to talk about the possibility of going home on Wednesday. Today was Friday and while this still felt a way off, it was something to aim for. Everything was going so well at last.

If we were to go home soon, I had to learn to clean and dress Bailey's stoma, so in came the stoma nurse to help me.

A stoma is basically when they divert the bowel to exit outside the body on the stomach, rather than via the bottom. So Bailey had what looked like a rolled up sausage on his lower left tummy, which then required a stoma bag to catch all the faeces. At this stage in the digestive tract, it isn't hard like poo, but a watery liquid.

When you clean the stoma, you must dry the area before sticking on the new bag otherwise it will leak. They're also prone to bursting if you forget to empty them.

It was a whole new world, but I was focused and willing to do all I could for Bailey. It was extending my mothering skills, if nothing else.

Back in the real world of home life, it was Harry and Mylo's school sports day. The boys and I had always planned for this to be Bailey's first outing, yet here we were stuck in hospital. Kev dutifully sent me through copious amounts of photos and videos of the boys' races, and I showed Bailey just so he saw their faces. They were his brothers and he had hardly spent any time with them yet.

My friend Emily visited today, along with my Mum, who basically came every day, God bless her. Emily arrived looking beautifully summery and given this was her first visit, like anyone who came by, she was noticeably emotional. She apologised for getting upset, saying she told herself she wouldn't cry in front of me. If I am honest, it made me feel better as it meant that I wasn't the only one that thought this was awful; that it really was as upsetting as I'd had myself believe. In her usual style, Em made me laugh and told me about her children's shenanigans and basically chatted superficial stuff, which was an absolute tonic.

Bailey was proving he was a fighter. He was powering on through and I felt so proud to be his mummy. That evening I went out for dinner with my mum and Kev's mum to the restaurant around the corner, Ciao Bella, while Bailey slept. While there, I noticed throughout the restaurant there was a myriad of books and photos with 'Bailey' all over them. It made me go cold, like it was some sort of sign, but goodness knows what exactly.

23rd June

Today Harry and Mylo came to visit their new baby brother. Not how I saw them spending time with him, but I felt so excited to see them that nothing would get me down. I had to remain strong for them while they were with us, as I didn't want them to worry or feel sad about anything. It was about making this exceptionally abnormal situation as normal as possible for them.

In true six and four-year-old boy style, they arrived with gusto. They were so elated to see Bailey and I had to stop myself from welling up as they threw their arms around me. It was a moment I had longed for and now I got to hold my big boys so tightly.

I expressed some milk so they could give Bailey his bottle, and then they pushed him in his pram down to the outdoor play area. They entered the brightly-coloured Disney-themed park, left the pram with me and ran off for some fun, their distant laughter being the most beautiful and welcome sound.

Watching them enjoy their visit made me feel so relieved as I didn't want this to be an upsetting experience for them. They were in their element, following the coloured paths and climbing on the boat. Meanwhile Bailey, Kev and I sat and enjoyed the fresh air and natural light.

We returned to the room and the boys had more big brother cuddles while making the most of our bedroom TV. I think they thought they were in a hotel. Kev bought us all some food, which we ate in the gardens, again the boys making the most of somewhere new and seemingly exciting to explore.

The moment I had been dreading arrived; it was time for Kev and the boys to leave so they could get to bed and ready for school the next day. My heart began to hurt once more and I did all I could to stop the tears from falling out of my welled-up eyes, swallowing deeply and quickly.

It was the most gorgeous day and I was so relieved it went well. I also felt relieved that all that happened next, occurred after their departure.

Alone once more, the doctors arrived to talk to me – never a good thing I was quickly learning, especially on a weekend when not many consultants were working.

Since the stoma had been created, they had been tightly monitoring the input (via milk) and the output quantity. This gives a gauge as to how effectively the stoma is working. In Bailey's case, the output was far too high.

"Mum, you have to stop breastfeeding and we are reverting back to two-hourly, measured bottle feeds. Bailey's stoma losses are just too high."

Shattered. Distraught. Crying.

Not just because it felt like so many steps backwards or because the news contrasted so much to my positive and enjoyable day so far, but because I knew deep down what it meant.

Many people who live with cystic fibrosis also have pancreatic insufficiency. Ultimately, this means that their pancreas doesn't produce the enzyme to break down and absorb nutrients from foods. Without the enzyme, food just passes straight through, also known as malabsorption.

If Bailey wasn't absorbing his food, it very likely meant he didn't have this enzyme, meaning it was even more plausible he had CF.

I had remained hopeful until this point, but my positivity in the five percent was starting to dwindle. I was running out of energy and so many things were stacking up against the outcome I so wished for.

I called Kev, sobbing down the phone, while he was bemused how things had changed so drastically in such a short space of time. This was the thing with the journey we were on – it was unpredictable, fast moving, uncontrollable and frightening.

Once in bed, I called my mum, and wasn't able to say much for crying, but it felt like she was next to me, comforting me just by being on the end of the phone.

24th June

I woke startled. Bailey wasn't in his bed. I jumped to my feet and rushed over to the High Dependency Unit and there I set eyes upon the most surprising and beautiful sight; Mum, sat in the armchair, holding her grandson while he slept. It was honestly the most idyllic picture and one I will treasure forever.

Mum knew I was upset, and she had come to see us and offer comfort and support. This was at 7am, so Mum had come all the way to London at the crack of dawn. She was our rock throughout this whole event, practically putting her whole life on hold to help us both at home with the boys and also support us in hospital. She had taken time off her job as a midwife and despite battling her own emotions attached to seeing her daughter go through so much heartache, remained a pillar of strength, in front of us at least.

The thing with genetics is that it affects the wider family. For example, if Bailey does have CF, then it means Kev and I both carry the gene, which means one or both of each of our parents also carry the gene, from whom we inherited it.

Then there were our siblings – did either my or Kev's sisters carry the gene, and if so, did their children? It's about your genetic heritage across your entire family tree, rippling out and affecting many lives.

Next on today's visiting list was my friend Lisa, who I knew through Kev's rugby. She is a Cognitive Behavioural Therapist, and I could tell while she was with me she was assessing things and trying a couple of techniques. I was actually grateful as at this point I would take any help on offer.

Later Kev's mum Mary and sister Clair arrived, bringing offerings of home cooked food. It was the best gift, being the first fresh food I had eaten since arriving ten days ago.

I did feel our room was becoming a conveyor belt for visitors, but in truth I needed the company as it was a welcome distraction from the trauma, monotony and plain four walls.

25th June

Monday morning and all the consultants and their entourages arrive after a weekend off. But this Monday the week really started with a stir.

The babies on the Chameleon ward are weighed every Monday, Wednesday and Friday, but today Bailey had lost another 200g on the scales. This was not good. They of course need and want to see weight gain, otherwise it's classed as 'failure to thrive', a term I distinctly loathe for many reasons, but predominantly because of how utterly negative it is.

This weight loss, teamed with the high stoma output, sent Bailey's entire medical team into overdrive, especially when it came to the notion of cystic fibrosis.

"Bailey won't be able to go home on Wednesday. It could be weeks. We will have to test his pancreas and we will put Bailey on a drip called Total

Parent Nutrition (TPN) so he can absorb the nutrients to help him grow and gain weight."

So much to take in, and all I could concentrate on was the throbbing pain in my heart.

"Any milk intake will be via a measured bottled so we can tightly monitor his intake, but you can continue one breastfeed each night to keep his latch and for comfort."

It felt like we had done a total U turn. The whole situation just reached a new level of grave – there was an air of urgency about the team and in Bailey's room and I felt really frightened.

After the big medical meeting with Bailey's consultant Dr Crosley, a nurse later came in; nurse Gertrude. I never took to this nurse, and now she was stood in my room telling me that we had to feed Bailey via NG tube to save his calories of effort used to physically drink the milk from a bottle.

Yet Dr Crosley had not mentioned this. I hated the idea and questioned it, but I was overwhelmed with information, medics and emotion, so I quite easily submitted to her demands.

Shortly after, I found the Cystic Fibrosis team in Bailey's room, which was another turn of events.

About a week prior, Bailey's surgical team had invited the CF team to come and talk to us. I had said I didn't want it as I couldn't take on anything I didn't need to know just yet, and the CF team had agreed, feeling it was unnecessary until we knew if Bailey had CF or not. So until now, the CF team were not in our lives.

Yet now they were stood in his room.

This is the point at which another very significant lady entered our lives; Claire. Claire and I were about to embark on a journey that I never wanted, indeed repelled, but I bless the day she became part of our story.

Claire was warm and friendly – she had a less medical and more personal air about her, tall with curly hair. She sat down and chatted to me on my level, clearly seeing how upset and shaken I was.

I wanted to ask her if she knew, if this was a classic case of cystic fibrosis. Did she know but just couldn't tell me until they had the facts in front of them from the blood test results? I can't remember if I asked her outright what she thought, or if I just stared at her so hard trying to read her mind.

"We are going to fast track Bailey's genetic blood test results for cystic fibrosis. We hope to have them by tomorrow."

I couldn't believe something that was going to take two weeks was now being done in a matter of days, if not hours. Claire said that if the result was positive, she would come back tomorrow joined by the CF fellow to discuss everything and answer our many questions.

Deep down, I knew what tomorrow was going to bring. I felt wracked with fear and sadness, and had an unshakeable sick feeling in my stomach.

Kev arrived that night for some daddy cuddles with Bailey, while mum babysat the older two boys. This was the only way we could see each other now – if someone came to our house to look after Harry and Mylo. As Kev held his youngest born, they put the NG tube into Bailey's nose and began feeding him like this from 8pm.

Kev left for home, having another late night before preparing the boy's school things, prepping his rugby work and getting to bed for another early start in the morning, which entailed sorting the boys, dropping them off at friends before school to enable him to get to work on time. I really felt like he was running around doing it all, and I was sat almost rotting in the armchair next to Bailey.

Once he'd gone, I had my one treasured daily breastfeed and lay down staring at the ceiling most of the night, wondering how tomorrow would play out.

26th June – Results Day

This morning was the worst morning. Not because of the test results that loomed over Bailey's head, but because he literally would not stop crying. He was screaming to the point of exhaustion, and no matter how much I tried to soothe and comfort him, I simply couldn't.

As a mother, the one thing you pride yourself on is being able to calm your child (most of the time). If someone else holds your baby, they grizzle so they pass the baby back to the mummy and hey presto, the baby settles. The familiar scent, sound of your voice and simple knowing is enough to pacify them. Unless they're hungry, of course.

This child was hungry and I knew it to my core. He had cried from 5:30am until 10:30am, which was so unlike Bailey. For everything he had been through, he seldom cried unless he was in pain. He didn't whinge for no reason.

My innate motherly protection rose inside of me and I found it within me to question that wretched nurse Gertrude who had put him on the NG tube.

"This isn't working. You put him on the NG tube to conserve calories from swallowing milk, and now he is burning ten times the amount of energy by crying. He's hungry and exhausted. Dr Crosley never said about the NG tube. I demand she comes here now and speaks to me and confirms if this tube is required."

Boom. I did it. I found my voice again amidst the emotion, overwhelm and unfamiliar medical environment. This rabbit in headlights transformed into warrior not to be messed with.

Soon Dr Crosley arrived with her minions swiftly on her tail and confirmed we were *not* to be feeding via an NG tube and she had not requested for such. I was elated! The tube came out, the bottle went in and the baby stopped crying. I'd got it right.

My mum arrived with a much-needed fresh-leaf tea from the coffee shop over the road – a real treat compared to the free tea from the hospital ward.

We sat drinking and chatting and then I saw two dark silhouettes standing outside our frosted-glass hospital room door. I checked the clock: 11am. My stomach dropped. A sick feeling like never before. I knew. In that moment I knew my son's fate was sealed.

They gently knocked, and in walked Claire and the gentleman she had mentioned. She knew by the look on my face that I had worked it out already, but she had to officially say the words.

"Laura, we have Bailey's blood test results back, and he has cystic fibrosis."

In these moments, it's hard to compute or retain how we felt or what we thought. I remember making a sound that was a cross between crying and screaming. I recall my whole body collapsing, and I almost saw myself from above, looking down on myself below, a bit like I had experienced when all this began at our local hospital.

Claire and her colleague stood outside while my mum comforted me. Is that what she did, or did she try to piece her daughter back together? Was she crying too, as she held me? What was she thinking? What was I thinking? It was just noise. My noise. My mouth trying to express the sheer, acute pain in my heart. My whole insides almost felt concave, like they were caving in. So much stuff was flashing before me; Bailey, our happy past, our uncertain future, our wedding, Harry and Mylo.

Harry and Mylo. Harry and Mylo. Could they possibly have it too?

I sat and I cried, for a very long time, with Claire waiting outside the door. Was she listening? Was I the parent with the worst reaction to this (somewhat obvious) news?

I was distraught. Not because I felt like I had an 'imperfect' son, or that I loved Bailey any less, but because I had yearned for this not to become a reality.

I had prayed with every fibre of my being that this would not be the outcome.

The guilt for giving this to Bailey engulfed me like a dark cloud that would remain for years, the grief set in and the fear took over.

I sobbed, for the lost hope and for what awaited my dear baby boy.

Claire returned to our room once I had calmed slightly, and sat next to me once again, warm and comforting.

She sifted through a leaflet on cystic fibrosis, which she said she would leave for me to read in my own time, but before she did, she opened at a certain page to show me a boy in his teens dressed head to toe in rugby kit, egg-shaped ball in hand.

"You see Laura, he can live a normal life. He can do everything his brothers do."

To this day I don't know if Claire consciously decided to show me that page. Was it sheer coincidence or did she know Bailey's daddy used to be a professional rugby player?

Unfortunately, I don't think it had the desired effect as I spun out again into hysterical crying. Not because I didn't think Bailey would play sport – quite the opposite as having a daddy like Kev would only serve him well. It was just all too close to home. I needed to get my head around it all.

Claire left me to wallow in my grief, and said the CF dietician would be coming to see us later today to help administer the Creon enzymes Bailey would now require with food for the rest of his life.

It's noticeably obvious that at this time, on a very important day, Kev was not at our side. He was (ironically following that picture) at work at Saracens rugby club.

Sport is a funny profession. The people in it aren't just doing a job; that is their life. Their lifestyle, if you will. Many like Kev play throughout their teens onwards, never having weekends off and only ever taking time off when it is the off season.

As mentioned, it was good fortune that Bailey arrived during his rugby off season, allowing him to be at GOSH with us for the first couple of weeks before his next pre-season began.

Kev could have asked, and was in fact offered, the opportunity to take off more time once they heard of our situation, but when I say Kev and I handled this situation differently, this is a prime example.

I needed Kev to go back to work, because I needed him. When he was off and at GOSH with us all the time, he started to lose his head, he stopped working out and he was falling down to my level. Once he was back at work, he was around the team, he wanted to train again and he was stronger and more positive when he then visited Bailey and me.

Plus, I needed him to be the parent there for our older boys. I felt that given I couldn't physically tear myself in two, the next best thing was for one parent to be at home and one to be at GOSH.

So while it seems odd to many that Kev wasn't there that day, it was what worked for us, and it worked well. In times of desperation, you do what works. You function on a different level – a basic level of survival. He had his outlet at work and the boys, while I had my mum and Bailey. It just worked for us, no judgement needed.

However, his absence meant that I now needed to call him to tell him the devastating news. As expected, he wasn't surprised, just gutted. He informed the club, and left rugby for the day to be with Bailey.

Kev arrived in time for the CF dietician's visit. She showed us how to use the Creon Bailey would require with foods containing fat and protein. These tiny beads that you scoop onto fruit puree and give him when he eats. It seemed crazy to me how something so small could have such a huge impact on someone's health and growth.

The CF team returned again to chat to both Kev and me. Kev already knew so much about it thanks to Google, following CF people on Instagram and messaging his cousin in Ireland. In contrast, I was in the dark. I deliberately hadn't looked at anything online and hadn't even dared to pick up the leaflet I had been given earlier today. I was far from ready.

Claire told us that we would have an educational day with the whole of the CF team, which comprised of her, the dietician, the physiotherapist, the consultant and the psychologist. We booked it in for next Wednesday 4th July when we knew Kev could be here.

They left, and then it was just Kev and me, with our thoughts, questions, fear, guilt, but overriding love, for our son and for each other. Kev turned to his phone to research, while I returned to the arm chair to look at our perfect boy.

Once Bailey had settled after his bottle feed, we headed out for some food followed by a drink in the pub opposite the hospital. We toasted Bailey, cystic fibrosis and all that awaited us. It wasn't a celebration, nor a commiseration. It was a marker; a starting point to our new normal.

Kev left for another late, long drive home before another frantic day, while I sat in the infamous arm chair giving Bailey his breastfeed. The comfort and closeness of this feed will always be in my memory. We both got some sleep, ready for a new day.

27th June

Bailey, it's how we respond to things – the cards we get dealt with in life and how we deal with them. You can choose to sink or swim; be a victim or a hero. You may be small my boy, but you shall be a hero!

You will use this to drive you and defy the odds.
You will be healthy.
You will do lots of sport.
You will laugh.
You will love and be loved.
You will be successful in whatever you do.
You will be who and what you want to be.
You will soar through life.
You will be positive.
You will be our light.
You will find strength beyond measure.
You will be a role model to others.
You will inspire.
You will be our hero.

This is what I truly see for you Bailey. We love you xx

As I sat writing this message to Bailey in my daily journal, I just prayed it would all be true.

Bailey had inherited two faulty CF genes, fact. One from me and one from Kev.

I feared CF, but I knew I must educate myself so this fear fades. Yet I still refused to go online, worried about what I might read. So I just kept jotting down my questions until our CF Education Day with the specialists on Bailey's team, who would now care for him until he turned sixteen.

Every morning I woke feeling like this situation was insurmountable. Like there was a cloud lingering above my head. Like my world – our world – has changed forever. I know and pray I will look back on this one day and feel silly for worrying so much. When Bailey is playing rugby with Harry and Mylo, football with his friends, running alongside me, swimming and excelling at school. That is what I truly see and believe for my son. And he has the world's best daddy to help him stay fit and healthy, as exercise is so important for people living with CF.

In this moment, we just need to find the strength and knowledge to come to terms with our new lifestyle.

My mum visited today, and she made me realise that I simply must go home to see Harry and Mylo. There was no telling how long we were going to be at GOSH now, so it was time.

It's the most unnatural feeling to leave your newborn child, but I was a mother to three children, so I must go and be a mother to my other two sons. I decided to leave Friday and I would collect the boys from school, while my mum agreed to be on granny duty and stay in the hospital overnight. Having my mum replace me was the only way I could leave Bailey – that was my condition and the only way I was walking out those hospital doors.

Dr Crosley visited, but despite more weight loss she was content with the stoma output, so hopefully the TPN and Creon were working. Friday's weigh-in would tell.

Kev's mum popped in, followed by my sister who came bearing gifts of home cooked vegetarian bolognaise, wine and dessert. We sat and ate, chatted and watched TV while I rocked a very hungry, unsettled baby. It felt like a relatively normal night – like we could have been in my lounge just hanging out. But the constant beeping, tubes, cold, sterile floor and nurses obs were a stark reminder that we were anywhere but home.

28th June

Today my mum and dad visited. My dad hates hospitals, so it was good if he could come with someone as I felt bad him having to come to somewhere he didn't feel comfortable. I knew he didn't mind and that he wanted to see us, but I still felt terrible.

I wasn't really sure if my dad knew totally what was going on. I only told him the main headlines, but I wondered if Mum was filling him in. To explain, my parents divorced when I was seven years old, but they have remained close friends, for which I always feel fortunate.

My dad kept referencing Bailey 'getting better' and 'growing out of it'. It frustrated me, but I also envied his ignorance, so I thought I would leave him in his own little bubble for a while longer.

While they were with Bailey and me, a male volunteer offered to sit in our room and play music for Bailey. I knew music was great for babies so although it was very unlike me as I was quite closed off, I gestured him in.

He sat down, playing on his guitar as I rocked Bailey. Tears rolled down my cheek and I remember feeling self-conscious with my mum and dad there. The music was soft and gentle, and made me realise how much we had missed. It had all been so chaotic, noisy, clinical and upsetting for the past two weeks. We should be in our warm cosy home, with lots of cuddles, music, baby toys and a safe, family environment.

Bailey had breathed in very little fresh air, he hadn't been out in his pram much, not walked the boys to school nor been out and about in the car. Did he travel well in the car seat or was he one of those ones who cried the whole way? I still had no idea.

My phone rang and it was the health visitor. She asked if I was home, at which point I explained Bailey's diagnosis and said he was now under the care of the CF team at GOSH. Of course she offered her support once I was home, but I felt she wasn't specialised enough for him now. I didn't hear from her again.

My dear friend Emily came to visit again too, bringing my favourite Pret food for lunch. I thoroughly enjoyed her visit and once she had gone I felt invigorated and strong enough to read the leaflet from Claire that still lay untouched on my side table.

It was useful, but simply raised a hundred more questions, which I feverishly wrote down in my notebook ready for the CF Education Day next week.

In what was turning into a room that resembled Piccadilly Circus, Kev arrived and he was the tonic I needed after that reading material; positive, pragmatic, re-energised. Due to his fitness experience, he had developed a fixation on how exercise would be Bailey's remedy. Of course, it would help, but I knew deep down it would only do so much.

Maybe Kev was hanging on to the one thing he could control and help with as a way to see this thing through. I let him have it, with neither the heart nor the energy to say otherwise. In the meantime, I would just pray he was right, like he'd been right about other things throughout our journey.

Tonight, I felt compelled to write again to our boy, Bailey.

You are Bailey. Bailey Barrett. You have CF, but you will not be labelled, nor will it define you. It is simply part of your genetic makeup – just like your blonde hair and blue eyes.

We will find a way to bring CF into our family, and enable it to sit alongside us all, without being engulfed by it. We will do physio and exercise together. We made you and we will ride every wave with you and do everything in our absolute power to build you up and make you strong.

You are so loved, and your big brothers adore you. I know they will always be at your side to cheer you on and protect you.

We are a family and we are stronger and more complete now you are with us. You will shine. You will be the example and the inspiration, of that I have no doubt.

Love you, Mummy xx

29th June – Great Ormond Street Hospital

As I was packing some bits into the bag that came in with me two weeks ago, I felt pangs of guilt and fear in my tummy. Today I was due to go home to see Harry and Mylo, leaving my mum and Bailey to hang out for the night.

I felt so guilty to leave my newborn son, and I also felt bad that my mum had to endure the hospital fold-out bed and plastic mattress, the smell of which I will never forget. It goes without saying how grateful we are to the epic NHS, but I can't big up their beds I'm afraid. However, thank you GOSH for giving parents a bed at their child's side; you rock my world! I didn't want to leave Bailey and I didn't want to do the school run to collect Harry and Mylo. We live in a small village so everyone knows everyone, more or less. I dreaded people asking me where Bailey was when I turned up empty handed, and I didn't know who knew what, which was giving me severe paranoia.

The wonderful Lisa came all the way up from our little village, simply so she could travel with me on the way back as she knew I was feeling anxious about it all. Maybe she would CBT me on route home and I would appear at the school gates strong and composed.

I moved my one-a-day breastfeed to 12 noon just before my departure, as I didn't want Bailey to miss out on his night feed completely. I left my mum holding my dear little boy, and let the door swing shut behind me.

As I started to walk away, carrying what was formerly just my hospital overnight bag, the past fifteen days were becoming a blur. I realised how unfamiliar the outside world had become; the buzz of the busy London streets, the train systems, the myriad of unknown faces, and the stark realisation that everyone else's life had been continuing. Mine had stopped back on 14th June, so I assumed the whole world had halted with me; Alas no. Just like the sun rose each morning and set each evening, so had the entire population with it.

Even my own family's lives had continued. The boys went to school, Kev went to rugby, all my family and friends went to work, watched rubbish TV and saw friends. It all just felt so surreal – like nothing they were doing truly mattered in life. Everything had lost significance.

Even money had lost importance. No amount of wealth could buy Bailey's health. We could have been the richest people in the world, but the outcome would be no different. It was a true lesson in the value of health, and life priorities.

For some reason I kept thinking my mum was going to walk in and make it all better. Make it all go away. I've no idea why, but I guess it's what mums do, isn't it? They make everything okay again. But not this time. This time mum could not help me, just like I could not help Bailey. I wonder if one day he would feel the same, and wonder why I'm not just making everything better for him?

29th June – Home

It was a dream to have Lisa as a chatty distraction on the train home. She drove me home from the station and dropped me off outside my house. The moment I turned that key and stepped in was the most surreal experience of my life thus far. It felt like I was stepping back into another world – my old life. It felt like I now had two lives – my life at GOSH and my home life. It felt like time had stood still, as if the past two weeks hadn't ever happened.

The kitchen calendar hung on the wall, still on the month of May, which hit me instantly. There were gifts, cards and flowers everywhere from Bailey's birth, many of which I had never been home to see. I felt a pang of sadness that we had not been able to enjoy them all, and nor had we been able to enjoy this lovely home.

I slowly walked around the house, which was quiet and still, and began to make my way upstairs. As I entered our bedroom, I saw Bailey's crib next to our bed. It was like a punch to the heart. The place Bailey should have spent every single night of his life, but yet only two nights so far. As tears rolled down my face, I wondered if Kev had left it there consciously, or simply hadn't even thought to move it while Bailey was absent for so long. Either way, I loved him for the fact he had left it right there, next to my side of the bed, ready for our return.

I wandered into Bailey's bedroom, where his pine wooden cot, soft blankets and copious amounts of teddies donated by his brothers all awaited him; all completely untouched. I yearned for the time we had lost. It looked so much warmer and cosier than where I now pictured him lying in a plastic hospital cot with their thin, overused blankets and one token teddy.

It was only one teddy, not because Bailey was only allowed just one, but because I was actually refusing to take too much stuff into the hospital. This was for two reasons. One, I was running on the utter core belief that he would be home soon, so why bother keep taking in loads of clothes, teddies and cards to just bring them all home again?

Secondly, I felt by something being at GOSH it would be tainted in my mind forever, so the less belongings we had in there, the more things I could enjoy once home, without it being tainted in any way, like a sour reminder. Ridiculous, I know, but I was functioning in the only way I knew how.

I had been savvy enough to have a shower at GOSH that morning, as I knew entering our shower room at home would just tip me over the edge, and I wanted to be strong and happy for the boys when I collected them. I knew I wouldn't be able to step foot in our shower room for a while, still haunted by the memories of seeing my green sick-covered bra – the moment it all began. I stared at myself in my bedroom mirror, long and hard; really looking intently into the eyes of the person before me. It was like looking at someone I didn't know; like I was looking into the mirror but someone else entirely different was staring back – just like the moment I had experienced at GOSH. I expressed some milk off, brushed my long, blonde hair and waited for the doorbell to ring. My two darling friends Hannah and Karen, whom I met in the village when our children all started school together, had walked to mine so we could all walk up to school together. Sisterhood at its finest.

I opened the door to their happy, yet trying-to-hide-it concerned faces, and bags of COOK food. This company is a dream for any mum looking for a healthy pre-made meal that you can throw in the oven and deliver child-standard goodness to their plates with ease. I stored them in the freezer with immense gratitude, stood tall, slid on my oversized sunglasses and walked the walk.

Head down, don't look at anyone and they won't ask you anything. Don't go too far in front girls as I'd rather you stuck with me. Let me just stand behind her here and then nobody can see me. Turn your head the other way otherwise they'll make eye contact. Walk faster, walk faster. Christ it's busy. I just want to get the boys and get home. Get them and get home; then it's job done.

This was my stream of the thoughts rolling though my head as we entered the school gates and to our children's classroom doors. We headed to collect our eldest children first, and as the doors flung open, there was Harry looking for his pickup.

The poor boys had been passed from pillar to post. Playdates with kind friends in the morning, after-school hangouts until Kev finished work, sometimes my mum was there, sometimes not. It was a piecemeal of childcare littered between family and friends so as not to burden any one person too much, nor ask too much despite everyone willing to help. Our family and friends were the glue that kept my family functioning at this time, as it simply wasn't possible just between Kev and I alone.

As Harry's big brown eyes scoured the nearby area for his collector, his eyes fell on me. I hadn't told them I was coming, partly to surprise them and partly in case anything went awry at the hospital with Bailey and I was unable to get away. My intent was to avoid potential disappointment and cause great elation.

He spied me and bounded over like a dog that hadn't seen its owner in weeks. I have never been held like that by Harry before, but it was a hug that poured up from deep within him. A hug he had longed for, apparently as much as I had longed for him from the other side of this forced separation. He held me for longer than what is classed a hug, making it an embrace that made my heart full and my knees weak.

But then my awful mummy error came to light.

"Where's Bailey? Is he at home with daddy?" he innocently asked.

I was back, and so therefore was Bailey. That was Harry's simple, and now seemingly-obvious thought process.

It wasn't something that had ever entered my head. I panicked, realising the mistake I had made and how I must now hurt this little man's heart to inform him that his baby brother was not in fact here with us, but I had left him at the hospital.

Christ, I still can't believe I actually left my new born. The guilt and fear of judgement was etched within me.

Back to the unfolding upset in the school playground ... Having wanted to remain inconspicuous during this pick up, it was becoming anything but.

Harry's enviable mummy hold was witnessed from afar and now he was crying and everyone was looking. Not at all how I planned. Total and utter fail on my part. How on earth had I not thought this through?

I coerced an upset Harry to collect Mylo from the classroom next door, and as my middle son rushed out for me, I swiftly informed him that Bailey was not here with me and that I was just surprising them with a visit home for the weekend. Thankfully Mylo accepted this at face value, and we all trundled home, averting eye contact or conversation with others as we went.

I shut the door behind me, locking out the world and all the faces I didn't want to see. Just my boys and I at home. No nurses, no machines, no beeping, but also no Bailey.

We snuggled up on the sofa until Kev returned from work with our treat night fish and chips. I drew out bedtime to spend as much time with the boys as I humanly could, laying in their beds listening to them read with an entirely new appreciation.

Bedtime can be so protracted and annoying when you're at the end of a long day. You just want the children to settle so you can crack on and clear up, do some work and enjoy a cosy night on the sofa. At least that's how I often admit to feeling.

Not this time. This time I savoured every laboured question, return visit and extra kiss. I would take all this love, affection and memory back with me to GOSH, and I would hold it within me to give me strength and happiness. I would draw upon these treasured moments to make me feel close to them when I wasn't.

The rest of the evening I spent soaking in the bath and relaxing with Kev. As I settled into bed and put my head on his chest as we held each other, I realised just how much I missed my husband. I missed our marriage, living together and his company. I missed our life. Our old life, in truth.

But now I also missed Bailey because he wasn't here with us.

How could you possibly desire to be in two places so much in equal measure? It didn't matter where I put myself, my maternal part would not rest until we were all back under one roof. This became my mission – my obsession if you will. I needed five people under this one roof, and then some sense of order would be restored into our lives again.

I slept terribly that night, and when Mylo came in early that morning I woke up thinking I was in Bailey's hospital room. Sadly, Great Ormond Street Hospital had now become my norm – waking at home felt alien, disorientating and alarming.

30th June

Of course I stayed in close contact with my mum while she was staying with Bailey, and she messaged to say he had been an angel all night. It made me feel at ease, and allowed me to enjoy my Saturday morning with the boys before I headed back.

I returned to normal life, running the boys to gymnastics and parties, and then in the afternoon it was their school summer fayre. I didn't relish going for all the questions, but I knew I had to be strong and also attend for the boys' sake.

As we ambled round the school grounds from one stall to the next, we met so many people we knew, who lovingly asked after our new baby boy, looking around for the pram.

"Oh Laura, how are you? Where is the new addition?"

"It's so lovely to see you. Can I see him?"

"Oh you're home. Where's Bailey?"

These caring questions were contrasted with the reactions of those friends that knew our situation. Heartfelt hugs, understanding looks, check-ins to see how we were all doing.

I was relieved once we could go, but on the other hand it meant it was time for me to leave the boys and head back to GOSH. As they dropped me at the station and I waved goodbye, my heart starting hurting again. I wondered if next time I came home it would be with Bailey?

When I returned to Bailey's room, Mum updated me and we sat and had a cup of tea together before she headed off. I hoped she knew how eternally grateful I would be for all her love and support.

That afternoon was quiet, as were most weekends at this hospital. You feel like you're biding your time until Monday when the consultants are back to take action. It felt nice but also gave me too much time to think.

My overriding emotion amongst the guilt and heartache, was fear.

I was afraid for Bailey and for our family. I was afraid of the unknown, of CF and what may happen, now and in years to come. I prayed it wasn't a 'bad case' of CF and that Bailey would fulfil a normal, active, healthy and long life, but I had also prayed it wasn't CF and He didn't hear me, so my faith was dwindling.

My emotions were creeping up on me and so I took to my journal.

I love you Bailey. Always know that. I am so, so sorry. My guilt is immense and plagues me daily. I honestly had no idea whatsoever and I hope you find it in your heart to forgive me. I'm truly sorry xxxx

1st July

July. Bailey arrived on 10th June and here we are at the turn of a new month and we were still in hospital with no real signs of being discharged.

Kev, Harry and Mylo bounded in to ease my Sunday. They fed Bailey his milk, stroked his head, chatted to him like he was one of their boy gang and held him while still hugely excited they could watch TV from the room.

It was these innocuous moments that made my heart both sing and hurt all at the same time.

The nurses allowed Bailey to come off his drip for an hour so the boys could push his pram to the Disney play area while they climbed and he got some fresh air and daylight onto his increasingly-pale skin.

As I sat in the brightly-coloured play area, I often found it hard to believe we were in central London. I thought the same later on when we sat in the 'Secret Garden' as the boys now called it. We seemed to have developed a ritual for their visits, and they looked forward to visiting and enjoyed themselves while here, but with each visit brought departure, and I know they found it hard like I did.

I could see Harry getting emotional as his big brown eyes began to well up.

"I managed to hold back my tears last time," he said.

My heart split a little further down the ever-expanding crevice. My biggest boy, my first born, trying to be strong amidst the storm. I didn't want him to be and nor did I want him to have to feel that he had to be.

I hugged him and told him there was no shame in crying and that he could cry with mummy and daddy whenever he needed. He didn't need to hold it in, nor be strong.

"Sometimes showing your weaknesses is strength," I whispered.

I held him and he sped off down the corridor to catch up with Kev and Mylo.

My wise words hung in the air, like a reminder to myself.

2nd July

The bustle of a Monday morning arrived once more, and the weighing scales rolled into Bailey's room.

I felt nervous and excited but as they put my little naked baby on the cold, white plastic scales, he showed an increase taking him back up to six pounds. Bailey was back to birth weight and I was so proud of him.

Bailey's medical team, who were lovely but appeared devoid of any excitement or emotional buy-in (which I totally understand), were quick to remind me this had been achieved predominantly by his drip. The task now was to slowly increase the milk intake and decrease the drip, in the hope Bailey would still gain weight.

The Legend, AKA Dr Crosley, advised we were now to do two thirds milk and one third drip. This totalled 31mls of milk every three hours, equivalent to two tablespoons.

My friend Amy was visiting today, along with our mutual friend Sarah. Our husbands had all played rugby together at Exeter Chiefs a few years back and we had become each other's Devonshire family while living in Exeter.

Sadly for Amy, she had just missed our visit from The Legend, so she would have to make do with Bailey cuddles. Sarah had travelled all the way up from Exeter where she was still living. I had insisted she mustn't, but like a true friend there she was in our time of need.

My other friend Katie also visited, another friend from the village whose son is Harry's best friend. She had the softest, most caring voice and expression I've experienced and it was so comforting to be with her.

Together the four of us laughed, cried and chatted. I knew how lucky I was to have such wonderful friends.

With Kev's visit later on that day, our room really was becoming quite the social hub. I kept wondering if so many visits were inappropriate or frowned upon by the staff, but what else were we do to with all this time?

3rd July

I made sure today was a quiet day as I thought tomorrow's CF Education Day would be quite gruelling and exhausting.

My dad visited in the morning so Bailey spent time in his big, warm arms, perched on his rotund beer belly. I often wondered what my dear dad thought of all this, but daren't ask as I just couldn't quite work out what he would say. The fact he was still suggesting it was something Bailey would grow out of or get better from showed that perhaps he wasn't fully accepting of what it was.

My friend on the ward Liana stuck her head into our room later that day. It was perfect timing as it was just Bailey and I so I was grateful for the company.

As I had hoped, I continued to bump into Liana on the ward since the day we met in the midwife's waiting room. We would often chat in the corridor to see how we were getting on, and sometimes we would get a cup of tea or sit by each other's child's bedside.

I cherished having found a friend at GOSH going through a similar experience, as I felt like we totally understood each other and what we were feeling and experiencing. Liana, who is Italian with strikingly dark hair which she always wore tied up and with a headband, seemed so strong and positive, which I wanted to absorb from her, but was equally mindful not to bring her down to my level.

We walked to the kitchenette to make a tea and then I went and sat with her by her daughter Sienna's bedside. Sienna and Ariella are twin sisters, but

Sienna was born with omphalocele, which is when the bowels are on the outside. The poor dear girl had endured multiple surgeries already with many more to go, to gradually get all the bowels on the inside before stitching up the wound for good.

With three older boys already at home, and a husband with his own business, Liana was unable to stay with Sienna at GOSH all the time. I wish she could, if only so we could hang out more. Yet she was always so together; so composed, organised and measured. I admired her hugely. When Liana wasn't there, I would sometimes check in on little Sienna for her, often looking so peaceful.

She was definitely the friendly face on our ward, having the biggest impact, chatting to the nurses, making friends with many mums and learning their stories through a genuine interest and care.

How could it be that I would be in London, and find a friend in someone who only lived twenty minutes from my home? They say some people are sent to you, and this was definitely the universe bringing her into my life.

4th July – CF Education Day

Just nine days ago Bailey had a confirmed diagnosis of cystic fibrosis. Today was the day we were due to meet all the team and learn exactly what this meant for his health, his future and our input as his parents.

Having read the leaflet provided this is what I knew so far:

Cystic fibrosis is a recessive genetic condition, meaning both parents need to carry the faulty gene to produce a child with CF. There are many different CF genes, with Delta F508 being the most common. Bailey had one of these genes, and the second was different. The life expectancy hovers around 47 years old.

People with CF have thicker mucus in their lungs, making them susceptible to frequent infections. These cause lung damage, which eventually lead to unhealthy lungs and possible need for a transplant. Stagnant water is bad for those with CF, because it harbours bad bacteria that can cause infections.

Other organs can be affected, such as the liver, and some people develop CF-related diabetes. Men's sperm is also much thicker, meaning its rare men can father a child naturally, not because their sperm isn't fertile, but because it can't travel to the egg to fertilise it. People with cystic fibrosis die too young. There is currently no cure.

That last learning sticks in my brain. There is no cure. It's like a life sentence.

My mum helped me understand the recessive genetic concept. A recessive genetic condition requires two CF genes to be inherited; one from each parent.

Bailey could have picked up neither of our CF genes, and we would be none the wiser that Kev and I carried the gene. Alternatively, he could have inherited just my CF gene or just Kev's while he was magically made through nature. This would have meant he was just a carrier of the gene – he only would have one CF gene and the opposing healthy gene would be dominant, so he would not be symptomatic of the condition, just a genetic carrier of the condition like Kev and I. Again, we all would have been blissfully unaware this whole thing extended throughout both our families.

Lastly, and the one which came to fruition, is that Bailey could pick up both parent's CF gene, meaning he has two CF genes. There is no dominant gene to override it, and that's it, he now has the incurable recessive genetic condition.

Whether Harry and Mylo are genetic carries of one of our genes, or have escaped the faulty gene altogether from both sides, remains to be known.

I had also read that one in twenty-four people carry the faulty CF gene. This means that when I met Kev twenty years ago at university, out of twenty-three other people in the line-up, we chose each other.

That was all I knew about the life-limiting genetic condition that was in my son.

Claire had advised me to write down any questions I had for this meeting, so I had been gathering them up over the past nine days. I didn't hold back – I wanted to know everything, from the serious to the ridiculous.

Am I allowed to kiss him on the lips?
Why does he get thick mucus in the lungs?
What does this mucus do to the lungs?
Once lung function reduces, can it be regained?
Will he have lots of hospital appointments?
Are the bacteria in stagnant water airborne or just from touch?
Can I still have real flowers or is water in a vase bad for him?
Are paddling pools OK?
Sandpits?

Splash parks?
Saunas?
Steam rooms?
Jacuzzis?
Mud?
If mud is bad for him, how can he possibly play rugby and football?
Can he paddle in our village stream?
How successful is meconium ileus at being flushed through?
Is the fact it didn't work a sign he has a bad case of CF?
What CF genes does he have?
Does cannabis oil help?
What is the life expectancy?
Do we still lose very young children from CF?
Is it okay to be near a fire/fire pit/bonfire?
Can I burn candles at home?
If my boys pick me wild flowers, am I allowed to keep them?
Should we now have a fake Christmas tree?
How do I differentiate between a common cough/cold and a cough that requires treatment?
Have my older boys got CF?
Will you sweat test them for me?
Why do I find this so catastrophic?
Is my reaction normal?
Do you all think I am irresponsible for not knowing?
What's the difference between a virus and bacteria?
What if something happens to Bailey when I'm not at GOSH?
What do I do with all his medicines when we fly somewhere?
Will he still be able to get health insurance?
Will he be able to get travel insurance?
Are stagnant toothbrushes bad for Bailey?
Can he go to the pub for a pint of beer with Kev, Harry and Mylo when he is older?
He needs a high-fat diet with additional salt, but how do I do this without impacting Harry and Mylo's healthy diet?
Is the stoma the cause of the high loss, or is that the CF? Or both?
Who cares for him once he is 16 and over?
I can't get away from my guilt. Please help me!
He will be so cross with us when he is older and understands what CF means for him.
How do I tell him about CF?

Can I buy a machine to check his lungs?
What do I look for when checking for lung infections?
Do all people with CF have lung infections?
Are tea towels a source of bad bacteria?
Sinks?
Toilet brush holders?
Sponges?
Bath toys?
Can he be with other babies?
Can he go to play groups?
Do I always have to give Creon on apple puree or is pear puree OK?
Will he be impotent as well as infertile?
The leaflet says he can get free IVF on the NHS. Is this just his first child or as many rounds for as many children as he so wishes?
If he has a child one day, and his partner is not a carrier of the CF gene, can he produce a CF child as he has two copies of the CF gene?
Can we have pets?
We have a cat. Can we keep her?
What do I do if friends have fish tanks/fish ponds?
Does he have to have Creon with snacks?
If I am breastfeeding, I don't know how much milk he is having, so how do I calculate how much Creon to give?
Are there any signs he has a bad case?
Can he be around smoky environments?
Can he wait in a doctors waiting room?
In your leaflet they mention physio equipment – what are they referring to exactly?
Can he swim in the sea?
Can he attend swimming lessons?
For his gene type, can you tell if it is a severe case?
Are his gene types easy or less easy to treat?
Are there benefits to being diagnosed so young?
Why is he more prone to infection and what type of infection do you mean?
If he doesn't get frequent infections, will he still get lung damage?
Will he have asthma?
Why do some get CF-related diabetes?
Is it true the life expectancy is 47?
Must the boys wash their hands all the time now?

Shall I wash my hands every time before I pick him up?
Should Kev shower when he gets home from rugby before picking up Bailey?
I was scanned at 20 and 38 weeks' gestation. Why was the meconium ileus not picked up on the scan?
Was my reduced fetal movement linked to all of this?
Is gene therapy a possibility?
Will he have other developmental or health issues?
Do you wean babies with CF differently?
Can he have Calpol?
If he loses salt, does he get thirstier?
If he takes ages eating his food, but Creon was given at the beginning, then how do I manage that? Does he require more Creon?
Why was the meconium ileus so bad?
Was there any way I could have known I/we carried the CF gene?
Was there anything I did while pregnant to cause this?
Is the gene from Kev any better/worse than the gene from me?
Is this lack of knowledge common for parents of CF children?
Why do we test for CF on day five newborn heel prick and not in utero?
Will my big boys become more prone to infection too?
How do I tell them?
What if Bailey resents his brothers for not having CF?
Is gene therapy an option for a cure?
How will Bailey ever forgive us?
Can he go to nursery at all?
If so, how will they know about his Creon?
Are there long-term effects of taking Creon?
Are there long-term effects of taking the Flucloxacillin antibiotic?
Should he take a probiotic to help his gut?
Is a drier climate, such as Spain, a better place to live?
Would it be beneficial to live by the sea?
At what lung function point would you resort to a lung transplant?

[Please know that you can find all the answers to these questions in Chapter 7 of the Support Guides if you are longing for answers to CF life like I was]

These were some of the hard, real thoughts going through my head as a third-time mum, but first-time mum to a child with cystic fibrosis. I was a mum third time round, and I felt like I knew nothing as to how to mother this child.

I craved information and knowledge. I craved answers to burning questions, some of which were burning a hole in my heart. I wanted to know all the answers, even if hearing those answers hurt my heart even more.

We had a running order for our day and one-by-one the specialists in their field came into our room, showering us with information that we would need to know for the rest of our lives, and that one day we would need to impart to Bailey.

Dietician

This lady, Lucy, told us about the requirement for a high-fat, high-salt diet, which seemed so alien having kept my boys away from these things to stay healthy. It seemed Bailey would be needing his own cupboard of treats, but how I justified this to the boys was going to be a challenge.

Despite the addition of having Creon enzymes, those with CF who are pancreas insufficient still have malabsorption, so never absorb one hundred percent of what they eat. Plus, they lose a lot of salt, meaning their skin is much saltier, hence the need to replace this through diet.

Bailey would be taking a daily multivitamin, a separate vitamin E and a dose of salty water called sodium chloride each day to aid his health.

Physiotherapist

Dressed in blue uniform, the physio showed us how to gently pat Bailey's back and chest, which would help alleviate the sticky mucus. Those with CF have much stickier mucus, which leads to frequent infections and consequent lung damage and reduced lung function. By loosening this sticky mucus, it helps them expel what they can. Physio and exercise are the tools for this, so while Bailey was a baby and sedentary, physio was vital.

We both tried patting Bailey's chest and back, mirroring the cupping action she had shown us, but I was being so gentle for fear of hurting him I doubt it was doing much. Could you imagine very firmly patting your three-week old baby?

Once home, we would progress to bouncing on a large Pilates ball, while using a PEP mask, once a day for fifteen minutes. A PEP mask has resistance to it, making the lungs work harder.

As the day progressed, I just kept thinking how alien this all felt and there was so much to take in.

Clinical Nurse Specialist (CNS)

This was Claire, who I was growing more familiar with each day. She was so lovely, but I was never too sure what she thought – she was hard to read. My question to her over this time was consistently, "Do you think it's a bad case of cystic fibrosis?" I would take a symptom, for example the meconium ileus, and ask if this meant his CF was a bad case. I craved the answer nobody could give me, because nobody knew. Two people with the same mutation type could have very different cases and experiences, so they simply couldn't answer my burning question.

I knew that Claire had become a big part of this process, and she would be someone we would see a lot of over the coming years, and I just needed to know I could trust her.

"If we are on this journey together Claire," I said, "I need to know you are being honest with me, even if it is something I don't want to hear. If I think you are lying to protect me, then I cannot trust you. I have to be able to trust everything you tell me. If you know he has a bad case, tell me. If you see signs this is bad, tell me. You must tell me everything. He is my son. I am his mother. I need to know you will tell me every little detail, no matter how hard it is for you to say and me to hear."

Claire's simple response was that she had told me all she could. Nothing else was definite. Only time would tell. She promised that she would remain honest with me, but how honest she intended to be only she knew. I loathed the idea of them talking about Bailey in their meetings, and I wasn't made privy to some of the information.

Consultant

This lady was the one Kev was ready to take on, asking questions about life-saving drugs, how far down the line research is and what Bailey might be eligible for based on his genotype.

She offered him optimism with information on clinical trials, drugs that were so close to coming to the UK and increased life expectancies.

To reiterate, at this time, the average life expectancy for someone living with CF is 47 years old. That's the average – it might be more, but equally it might be much less. If someone told you your child was to only live until 47, how would you feel? Or what if you were to only live to 47. How many years would you have left? Or would you already have passed away? It's such an alarming thought and I can't imagine what it's like to live with an age above your name.

Another startling thought – that someone, somewhere, has inadvertently put a price on your life. Whatever the cost of the medicine, is ultimately what your life is worth.

Orkambi, one such wonder drug, was not here in the UK, despite being in Ireland and USA for a number of years. The consultant explained that the Cystic Fibrosis Trust were battling with the government and Vertex to find a way to bring it to UK market at an affordable cost.

Whether or not Orkambi was in the UK, it was not suitable for Bailey's genotype, so talk about it as they may, it had no relevance to our son's case.

Psychologist

I doubt this lady knew where to begin with me. I was nothing short of an emotional mess, both for the trauma we'd endured and the diagnosis we had started to become familiar with.

I wanted to talk to her about a whole myriad of things, but in contrast Kev was saying very little, so I held back slightly. I angled my questions to be about the boys, rather than my own feelings of guilt, fear and doubt. I sought advice as to how I tell the boys about Bailey's CF, how I tell Bailey when he is old enough, how we bring it into our lives without letting it consume our lives. It was helpful and she was kind, but there was so much I didn't talk about.

Once we'd reached the end of our schedule, Kev and I were left alone in our room. I could have physically collapsed. I felt drained, exhausted and overwhelmed.

In contrast Kev declared his hunger, reached for a protein bar and said, "Well I thought that went well, don't you?"

I could have fallen to the ground. My jaw certainly fell to the floor. Were we even in the same meeting all day? How on earth had he come to this succinct and positive conclusion? How could we be presented with the same information by the same people and feel so utterly different? Another case of our acutely opposite approaches and viewpoints on this entire journey.

I just slumped on my small, plastic camp bed and cried. I hated today, I hated CF, I hated this room, I hated myself for what I had done to Bailey and our family, I hated the crappy clothes I was wearing, I hated the smell of myself and I hated that I couldn't find my way so strongly and positively like Kev.

Still concerned by his empty stomach, Kev bounded out of the room on the hunt for some decent food with such optimism for Bailey's future that I didn't know if I envied him, or felt sorry for him for the fall that I believed awaited him.

I prayed our extremes would one day balance out and provide a strong base for Bailey and the boys.

I skipped tea that night. I felt done in, to the core. This was worse than I ever thought, and I had never been so out of control of my own life.

5th July

It was a room full of visitors today with my sister Jules coming to see us, plus friends Gemma and Lesley.

Each day, while Bailey had one hour off his drip, I would take him outside in his pram for some fresh air and sunshine. It always felt so good and I never wanted to return.

In the evenings, I often just sat and held Bailey, looking at his perfect face, wondering how it was possible there were any complications inside his little body. The one good thing from this situation was that I was able to sit and cuddle my baby boy far more than I ever would have done if I were at home. I had no cleaning, cooking or tidying up to do. I just sat quietly, alone, holding him, overthinking today, tomorrow and the next few decades.

This evening, I opened up my social media apps on my phone for the first time since proudly announcing Bailey's birth back on 10th June.

Since I had arrived I hadn't so much as glanced at Facebook or Instagram. I think it was because it meant that the world was still going round and everyone's lives continued. I'm unsure why I decided to go on today but I did, simply to post a beautiful photo of my baby boy. Normally feeds would be overflowing with newborn baby photos, but mine had been deadly silent.

As Instagram opened, I tentatively scrolled through my news feed. I hated it, and wished I had never clicked the icon. It all felt so superficial – so egotistical and pointless. Who cares what you ate for dinner or that you worked out? Why are you moaning about having your children at home for the six-week summer holiday? That was currently my absolute goal; to be home in time for when the boys broke up from school on 20th July and I would literally immerse myself in their company being their mummy. In my moment of discontent, I unfollowed so many people I had pointlessly allowed to fill my feed.

I stopped scrolling and focused on my purpose of coming on here; to showcase my baby. I carefully chose a photo that was just a beautiful facial shot, with all tubes and any tell-tale hospital signs out of sight. I didn't want anyone to know about our plight who I hadn't already told. I can't explain why. With nothing but Bailey's beautiful face and a little blue heart emoji, I shared our little one with the world, hiding the truth about our situation. It's amazing what you can falsely put on social media.

I didn't return to social media for quite some time.

6th July

Today was Kev's thirty-eighth birthday, and his gift from Bailey was a weight increase and going up to 45mls of milk per feed, reducing the drip in line with that.

Bailey was proving what a fighter he was and we were all so proud. It felt reassuring as I trusted in him to kick butt to CF and thrive beyond all the odds set out before him.

Given it was my husband's birthday, I fulfilled my weekly Friday ritual of returning home to see the boys while mum came in to stay with Bailey overnight. I dutiful changed the sheets on my camp bed and brought mum up to speed on everything before I departed.

This week my friend Donna came in to visit so she could travel home with me and we could collect our children from school. I was so excited to see the boys again at the school gates, and I was starting to feel more confident out in public without Bailey.

As Donna and I arrived at St Pancras train station my heart sank; all the screens were flashing CANCELLED next to every single train out of London. What on earth was going on? I felt so desperate to get back and not disappoint the boys, but I was literally stranded.

We resorted to a very costly taxi, which was also slow moving as everyone had done the same so the traffic was a nightmare. With two minutes to spare, the taxi pulled up outside the school gates and Donna and I pegged it to the class rooms to collect our little people.

To hold my boys, to see their faces and feel their embrace once more as they bounded out from their school day was something so special. If you think how you feel after a few hours of not seeing the children, now imagine an enforced week. It was just worth every penny spent on that taxi.

That night the four of us went out for Kev's birthday meal. It was a beautiful sunny evening so we went to a pub restaurant with lots of outdoor seating. The boys were playing on the stationary tractor while Kev and I looked on from our seats. It was a beautiful and welcome change of scenery and I stored the sounds of their laughs firmly in my head so I could call upon them when I wasn't with them.

There was a family on the table next to ours with a tiny newborn, and I couldn't help but think how unfair it felt that Bailey wasn't here. How could we continue as normal here, while he was enduring everything back at GOSH? The guilt swept over me, but then I tried to bring myself back to the moment and focus on the three boys before me while I was close to them.

I put the boys to bed that night and spent time with them cuddled up and reading, and then my eyes fell on the hand and foot prints I had done for them when they were babies. Each were done at three weeks old – I felt so sad for the time we had lost together. Bailey was now four weeks old and his prints weren't done, he had slept in his crib only twice, been in the car twice, slept on Kev's chest once and not yet had a bath.

Of course the nurses at Great Ormond Street Hospital offered to bath Bailey, and were always encouraging me to do so. However, having a bath with Bailey was something the boys had been so excited about, so I was waiting until he came home. I wanted his first bath to be a special one with his brothers.

It sounds crazy, I know, but I suppose it feels like an element of control – those tiny small things that I get to decide, like expressing breast milk and the lack of teddies.

7th July

I spent a lovely day taking the boys to their various activities, bike riding with them, and then it was time to head back into GOSH.

Bailey had been as good as gold for his granny. I expressed some milk and then sat back down, and waited. Waited for Monday to roll around. Waited for the weekend to pass so someone could tell me more about what was going to happen. Waited for us to be able to go home. Waited.

8th July

Bailey's big brothers bounded in for another Sunday visit, and excitedly had cuddles, put the TV on, pushed the pram and enjoyed the play area once more.

I loved them being here as it made the time pass quicker, and I believed it must be so good for Bailey to hear their voices and feel their presence. I hoped he knew how much they loved him. The way they look at him when they hold him; it's utter adoration. It's unconditional love, of that I know for sure.

Once they were gone, I realised we had been here almost a month. A month! If someone had told me that I would still be here in four weeks when I had arrived, I would have laughed in their face. Anyway, we are here and I must find gratitude that we've had the best help and things appear to be calming down and moving in the right direction to getting home. Or so I thought …

9th July

Another weigh-in Monday and no weight gain. No loss, but no gain. I was gutted. I knew this meant we wouldn't be going home on Friday like I'd secretly hoped.

Dr Crosley did her rounds and confirmed that Bailey had to stay on his drip until Wednesday. Until Bailey could put on weight (aka 'thrive') on milk alone, without any assistance from a drip, then he had to stay in.

True to form, I cried.

Dr Crosley reassured me that we weren't still at GOSH due to Bailey's CF – this could be managed from home. It was now all to do with Bailey's weight and gaining weight through milk. The issues were being caused by the stoma. It was located quite high up his ileum, which meant there was little digestive tract to allow him to absorb all the goodness from the milk, even with the Creon enzymes he needed.

So although he has cystic fibrosis, it was not this that was keeping us in this situation.

I often wondered what Dr Crosley thought of me. Not in an egotistical way, but because she gave so little away, as did all these specialists. I had put her on a pedestal, and to me what she said was gospel, so I hung on her every word.

This drove me to ask a lot of questions. Just like I had all my cystic fibrosis-related questions for the CF team (of which were ongoing as every day I thought of something else), I had multiple daily questions for Dr Crosley.

I always feel better if I know things – sitting and wondering is like slow torture for me. Throughout this whole thing I realised how much I relished information and facts, and then I could wrap my head around the new knowledge and move forwards.

I had been an emotional wreck the entire time I had been in this place, and The Legend had seen me at my lowest and darkest points. I was getting stronger, but I was an impatient soul who simply wanted to get her son home.

I was desperate to get home, but for what? To see him fail to thrive? To go home to simply get re-admitted would be worse than just staying put. Why did I want to rush my baby home if he wasn't gaining weight or considered 'healthy'? My head was so muddled.

I could tell that Dr Crosley respected my questions and desire for knowledge and to be informed, but goodness I wish I could read her mind and hear what she says about our case to her team in private meetings.

My spirits perked up with a visit from my friend Anna and then Bailey's grandad came in for more cuddles.

Later those friendly faces were replaced with the increasingly familiar faces of the CF team. First the physiotherapist came to check how we were doing with Bailey's patting, and then Claire came by to answer another page full of questions.

I asked why she thought we were still in hospital, and she agreed it was nothing to do with Bailey's CF. If he was gaining weight, we would have gone home a long time ago. It was a mix of frustration and reassurance. I was literally obsessed with getting us home; from the second I woke to the moment I fell asleep, it consumed me.

My mind was racing and the walls were closing in on me, so while Bailey was off his drip I took him for a stroll. He fell asleep so I sat down and ordered myself a drink in the sun in the nearby café. I felt tired and deflated. I knew I was running out of energy, but I couldn't afford to stop yet. I had to keep going. I had to stay standing.

That night, I turned to my journal.

Bailey, I am so, so sorry. I simply didn't know. I had no idea about CF, how people get it and certainly not that daddy and I are carriers of it. I think about all the things I will need to tell you one day when you get older, and right now I have no idea what I will say. I don't blame you if you're cross with us. I don't blame you if you're mad you have CF and none of us do. It sucks, I know. And believe me, if I could take your CF genes and give them to myself, I would in less than a heartbeat, because you have so much living to do. But sadly I can't. All I can do my darling boy, is promise to look after you, be your role model and inspiration, and love you unconditionally, as I do. And please know, through all of this, I am always at your side, now and always. Mummy xx

10th July

Bailey turned one month old today, and what a month it has been for this poor little fella.

I've been so busy looking forward, but today I took time to look back and recall the catalogue of events that have occurred in such a short space of time.

We wouldn't have been able to keep our family of five going without the support we received from family and friends. They say it takes a village to raise a child, but it also takes a village to save a family, and our village friends were out of this world. Kev received regular deliveries of home-cooked food for him and the boys, people looked after the boys before and after school, our family would stay at our house for a few days to do school runs and after care while Kev was at work, plus many people came to visit us here in London.

They were all the glue that kept our family going both emotionally and practically. I felt so humbled and privileged to have such an amazing network of support around us.

Our family and friends were our biggest blessing and I wish I could do something beyond words to express our gratitude to them.

11th July

Bailey simply maintained his weight today – no loss, but no gain. I felt so sad that he was struggling so much to grow, and began wondering if there would be long-term implications.

Dr Crosley agreed to take Bailey off the drip and see how he went on just milk, however I could tell she was hesitant to do this and I did not feel at all confident of the outcome at the next weigh-in on Friday.

Dr Crosley needed to liaise with the CF team to check they would increase his Creon dose per milk feed to counteract some of the obvious malabsorption, which they did.

However, I was starting to feel like Bailey was caught in the middle. He was on a surgical ward rather than the CF ward, because when he was brought in we didn't know he had CF and he was being looked after by the team who would operate.

With each step we took, the two teams needed to liaise and agree. Sometimes it just felt like the cha-cha – three steps forward, one step back. It wasn't anyone's fault of course, but they all had different approaches and opinions based on their speciality and focus for Bailey, and I wasn't sure who had the overriding say.

When the psychologist visited later that day to see how I was holding up, I explained how I was feeling about the situation between the two teams. It seemed to add time to each process and there was so many people involved in Bailey's current care that it felt complicated.

Something was rising in me that I hadn't felt for a while, and that was the desire to stand up for my boy and fight. If we weren't here for the fact he had cystic fibrosis, then we had to find a way to get this stoma to work efficiently and then we could go home and do the rest from there.

So I called a multi-disciplinary meeting. This is a meeting where everyone caring for Bailey gets together around a table to discuss a common approach to ensure all members are working together.

I was nervous, I had no idea what I was going to say or what they would say to me, but I wanted both of Bailey's teams in the same room at the same time to talk about best steps forwards. To discuss together the actions we must take collaboratively, to give this child a fighting chance of thriving and getting out of here.

The date was set for the following Thursday 19th July. It was time to pull up my big mumma pants and start being Bailey's voice once more.

My sister visited today and brought lots of yummy treats and I really enjoyed her company. Jules was doing so much for us; having the boys when she could and visiting us here, all with three children of her own and working as a PE teacher.

Later Kev came in and cuddled Bailey while he watched the football on TV. It was a lovely sight and they were both so content. I prayed Bailey recognised Kev after all his efforts to visit as much as he could while working, managing the house and taking care of Harry and Mylo. He really had stepped up to the plate and was looking so tired. In contrast I felt like all I did was sit in this chair and pump milk.

Afterwards I emptied Bailey's stoma bag and my heart dropped. It was so full and it was such a watery consistency. I knew immediately that things weren't going well on just milk feeds, and felt so deflated. I told the nurse, but we had to wait for Dr Crosley in the morning.

12th July

As I predicted, Dr Crosley was not happy with Bailey's stoma output. She wanted to decrease Bailey's milk intake unless the CF team increased Bailey's Creon dose.

I knew the Creon dose was already on the high side following previous conversations, so I wasn't sure what they would say. However, they agreed to increase the Creon to improve Bailey's absorption, but if this wasn't enough, where did that leave us?

This feeling of the two teams trying to work together coherently but with different agendas and goals seemed to becoming more emphasised the worse the situation got.

The nurses were also pressurising me to bath Bailey, but I simply didn't want to. I wanted and needed to hold onto the hope that his first bath would be as the boys had dreamed; at home with them surrounded by bubbles. Naturally, I cried and they submitted.

I later met Liana for a cup of tea, which was a breath of positivity and comfort. I loved meeting up with her for chats and telling each other about the latest antics of our children's wellbeing. We just got each other. The only difference I always felt was that Sienna would one day go home and lead a normal life. Bailey would go home and still have a lifelong battle before him.

Great Ormond Street Hospital is the saddest place in the world. We were blessed to be under the best care England has to offer, but no parent wants to wind up here. If you're here, it's because you have a sick child and nobody wants that.

I would wander corridors and see parents collapse with emotion, crying, hugging and even kicking a wall. The place was filled with frustration, heartache and sadness, mixed with tinges of optimism and gratitude.

It sounds terrible, but I would often find myself comparing situations with others, asking myself would I rather be in their shoes or my own? Would we be better off with this ailment or condition, or what Bailey has? I know this sounds like such an awful thing to say, but that place, especially being there so long, does strange things to your head.

When I saw other children, I remained thankful that Bailey was able-bodied and would be active and mobile once old enough. He looked like the perfect baby, and would go to school one day and nobody would ever be able to tell what he went through nor the life-long condition he carried. He would be just like all the other children, and I held on to this knowledge closely.

The word 'incurable' always re-entered my head soon enough though.

My friend Lucy travelled all the way up from Exeter today, and she was an absolute tonic. She always knows what to say, but adds dashes of humour along the way.

When I had my first son Harry, Lucy gave me a necklace with his name on it and I wore it daily. I then updated it with Mylo's name when he was born, and now Lucy arrived with my more recent version, featuring all three boys' names. I was delighted and quickly put it on.

The smallest of things made the biggest of differences in these situations, and having Bailey's name on my necklace at last just made me feel at ease – like I was doing the exact same steps for him as I had done for the others. Treating him like an equal, as I promised I always would. There would be no exceptions for Bailey.

My necklace now bore the names of all three of my sons and Kev's. They might not be together physically just yet, but all their names were close to my heart, and it was the second best thing.

I love you all so much, and my world is full, rich and happy with daddy and you three boys in my life. This experience will bring us all closer together, even if right now we are torn between two locations. It's only a few miles, but we could be on either sides of the world and it would hurt just as much.

As I put my journal and pen down, I checked Bailey's stoma output on the chart outside his room. As I've mentioned, I had zero medical knowledge when I came in here, yet now here I was reading the workings out of a stoma output. I could also calculate that they were far too high, and that tomorrow was not going to be a great weigh-in. I went to sleep feeling nervous for the morning.

13th July

Friday 13th – I've had some good ones and some bad ones. This time around, it was a bad one.

No weight gain and a stoma that was literally flooding out. That's now a whole week without any weight gain on a four-week old baby. Anyone who's anyone knows that's not good news. Why could my baby not grow?

Today was also the day of the week I was meant to return home to see Harry and Mylo. As usual, I was due to collect them from school, and this week Emily had come in to take the train home with me. Yet Dr Crosley had not been and I knew things weren't looking good, so I had to stay. I was so gutted and had no idea what I would tell the boys, but I knew I would still try to make it home tonight, depending on the outcome here.

As Emily left our room, I was heartbroken not to be leaving with her, but I made the right decision. It got to 5pm and in came Dr Crosley, with some gut wrenching news.

"The stoma output is still far too high and Bailey's weight gain is not enough to thrive. If we can't find a way to stabilise the output and help the weight gain, you may have to stay here until we can reverse the stoma. However, I can't reverse the stoma until about eight weeks after his previous operation."

Oh. My. Goodness. That was another month away. We might have to stay in here another month! This was insane. My head was whirring, my eyes welling up and my body was overheating.

But then there was another sensation. Relief.

If we didn't go home, it meant I wouldn't have to go home with a stoma – only a normal working bottom. It also meant I wasn't unduly putting my son at risk, and wouldn't fear being re-admitted at any moment. It meant Bailey would continue to be closely monitored and helped by the top specialists London had to offer. Why was I so keen to escape their aid?

What was I thinking? Was I becoming institutionalised? Was GOSH now my safety blanket rather than my hell?

My mind was spinning, and all I knew was I had to get out of here, run for a train to get home and see Harry and Mylo before bedtime. I arrived at home, hot and flustered but I made it; I got to see my big boys before they went to sleep. I hadn't completely let them down – only partially – and today that was a positive I was going to take.

I later soaked in the bath, chatting to Kev about all that Dr Crosley had said. I explained my mixed emotions about not wanting to stay but then feeling a sense of relief, and for the first time in over a month, we were approaching this from the same direction. He agreed he could see the reason and benefits of Bailey staying in for now.

I went to bed that night in clean pyjamas, next to my husband, with my big boys just next door and Bailey's empty crib still by my bed.

14th July

I spent the morning with the boys doing various activities, bike rides and baby chino stops, but soon I found myself back at GOSH.

I whiled the day away thinking about the multi-disciplinary meeting we had in a few days. I had started the process for this because I needed the two teams to work more collaboratively to achieve the goal of getting Bailey home. Yet now I was wondering if this was the best thing for my son.

It might be what I want, in an ideal world as a mother to three children, but if I forgot about everyone other than Bailey, what was the best thing for him? Deep down I knew the answer, even if I didn't like it, which then left me wandering what battle I was fighting next Thursday.

Kev's sister Clair arrived that evening for some much-needed chat and distraction. We went to Ciao Bella next door for some lovely pasta and a glass of wine. I was so glad for the company as I think I would have festered alone in my own thoughts had she not visited. We chatted about her work and two young children, and I mentioned about all the Bailey signs and books in the restaurant, which I still found so strikingly strange.

It was a lovely evening, but as we walked back to the hospital, I felt sad that she was getting the train back home to her family, while I was back inside the four walls.

I simply had a constant ache in my heart, for so many reasons.

15th July

The boys' Sunday visit was here again – another week in here, another week apart. The usual fun was had, but the goodbyes hurt all of us more today.

Harry didn't want to go home at first, and then he wanted us to go with him. It made me realise how confusing this must be for their six and four-year-old brains. So much to take in, so much change. Of course a new baby brings change, but this was so drastic I hoped they wouldn't be impacted long term in any way.

Everyone was missing each other, and we were all tiring of this hopeless situation that seemed to have no end.

Harry's rosy face and shiny, wet brown eyes made my heart break. In contrast, Mylo was just quiet, and I worried what was going on in his little head. I could have picked up Bailey and walked out all five of us. But I knew. I knew we were here for a while yet and I had to find a way to manage this situation.

I also knew all weekend that Bailey's stoma output was far too high, and that a weight gain tomorrow was looking increasingly unlikely.

16th July

A loss. Bailey's weight was dropping down and I felt shattered.

The reason I fought so hard to continue breastfeeding (even if this was via a bottle of expressed milk) was because I believed to my core that the best nutrition Bailey could have was my breastmilk. Midwives say it all the time, hence the pressure women feel to fulfil this role. It goes without saying that I do not agree with this pressure, as I, like most, believe 'fed is best'.

However, after weeks of three-hourly expressing and a commitment to it that astounded some of the top breastfeeding specialists, it seemed my efforts to feed Bailey breastmilk were pointless. I had sat almost attached to that yellow Medela pump since the day I arrived, yet here I was with a baby that could not grow on my milk.

Rationally, I knew this was down to the inner workings of his stoma, but irrationally as an emotional mother, I felt defeated.

Totally shattered by yet another weight loss, a new plan needed to be devised. Dr Crosley wanted to increase the Creon to stop malabsorption, but the CF team didn't want to, so instead recommended an antacid to help the efficacy of the Creon. Additionally, Dr Crosley put Bailey on an Imodium to help prevent the stoma output.

My six-week old baby's 9am feed now also included iron, vitamin E, a multivitamin, antacid, sodium chloride, Flucloxacillin and multiple scoops of Creon throughout the day.

This isn't much for some mothers of children with other ailments I know, but as one who previously shied away from Paracetamol, this was a lot.

Unconditional Love

My dad came in today to sit with Bailey while I went to St Guys and Thomas Hospital to have a blood test. My copious amounts of frozen breastmilk from my excessive pumping was taking up too much room in the hospital freezer (four large drawers to be precise). I knew Bailey would never get to use this milk, especially as I hoped one day to just return to normal, uncontrolled breastfeeding. So I had decided to donate most of it to the neonatal babies in the hope my efforts would help other children who needed it.

When I arrived back from the blood test, Bailey's overflowing stoma bag had exploded all over dad's smart shirt. My dad always wore a shirt to visit Bailey, just like he always put on a clean shirt for dinner at home. He had the sweetest, old school traditions, and I loved that he dressed up to see our boy.

As I walked back into the room, I was met with the sight of the nurse changing Bailey's stoma bag, and dad's shirt covered in brown liquid, which he was trying to wipe down with a paper towel. Far from ideal and in some ways quite comical.

Yet I felt an odd pang of embarrassment. Embarrassed I had not emptied the bag before I left. Embarrassed that we were in this situation. Embarrassed that my dad was now covered in my son's faeces. Embarrassed the nurse had to change the bag and I wasn't here to do it, as his mother.

I cried a lot today, and I could also feel my simmering hesitation to go home increase, in case it all went wrong once we got back.

Soon Kev arrived for some late night cuddles with Bailey. I admired his commitment to his family, his days starting so early and finishing so late.

17th July

Having been so upset on the phone to my mum last night, she whizzed in today to see us unexpectedly.

Mum whizzes everywhere. She is always in a rush, always walks quickly and everywhere only ever takes an hour to get to (even if it's two hours in reality). She is the most selfless, caring, giving person I have the honour of knowing, and the fact I get to call her my mum is one of my greatest life blessings.

She has always been there for me, but as a stanchly independent person, I've often been off doing my own thing, leaving home at eighteen for university and never returning. Now, when I was at my weakest but needing to be my strongest, there she was.

Every time I needed her, she would drop what she was doing and come to our side. She said the right thing, she backed off when needed and she stepped up when wanted. She read me and the situation perfectly, and I only prayed she knew the depths of our gratitude for her help. Mum always came in strong, fresh faced and looking her usual beautifully-dressed self. Yet I always wondered what went on in her head and how she was coping away from my sight. The fact she is a midwife and noticed the sick, the fact she does the day five heel prick tests for all her women, the fact she had lived and breathed every moment of this with us. Surely it was all taking its toll on her too?

Fundamentally, just like I couldn't help my child, nor could she help her daughter. My mum was as helpless a parent as I was. Were our maternal feelings being mirrored – guilt, helplessness, love, fear? I only hoped her pain was less than mine.

18th July

Wednesday weigh-in day and a gain. I couldn't believe it, yet I didn't feel the elation I expected.

Bailey needed to gain a significant amount of weight, because he was now so far behind the growth chart that he wasn't even on a percentile. A mere 200g increase wasn't going to cut it. If he had to work this hard to gain such a small amount, were we working in his best interest? Should he be on a drip as well? Should we be aiming to go home any time soon?

Again, my mind wandered to tomorrow's meeting and what I was pushing for. I was beginning to feel like my plea might be doing a U turn.

Today was Mylo's final Reception assembly and I had promised him that I would be there. So following a request for an early weigh-in, I bolted for the 7am train home, and made it just in time to see my middle boy perform on stage. Oh the pride I felt for this dear boy, but I felt distracted from this life now – like I couldn't settle or sit still.

I had planned for my sister to come into GOSH as soon as she could after dropping her children off at school, so once I got back to Bailey's bedside, dear Jules was there. Later Kev's mum visited bearing food-based gifts and welcome chats. I was so grateful for all their love and support.

I had kept the afternoon free to prep for tomorrow's multi-disciplinary meeting between Bailey's surgical team, CF team and myself; his mother.

I prepared some questions and thoughts I wanted to talk through, and then I walked to a nearby shop to buy myself a blouse and blazer to wear. I wanted to be taken seriously, and I needed to up my game. New clothes, washed hair and a renewed outlook on what I wanted to come from this meeting set me in good stead.

19th July

The music man came to play some songs to Bailey this morning, which he really responded to. I definitely feel he is more aware and developing, which is so wonderful to see.

Afterwards, I took Bailey for a walk and while he slept I sat in the sun, thinking about what to say and visualising how I wanted the day to go.

I put on my new clothes and some make-up, and hoped they would take me more seriously today, compared to the emotional wreck they had previously witnessed. I was nervous as I thought it would be intimating.

All the specialists gathered in the meeting room and discussed between themselves first, and then the nurse came to collect me to invite me to join them. I followed her to the meeting room and as I walked in, so many faces stared back at me. Some I knew, like Dr Crosley and some of her team and then of course members of the CF team, but then there were many faces I didn't know too. Most were dressed in normal attire, rather than uniform, which made me thankful for my new clothes. Dr Crosley appeared to be the leader of this meeting, but now it was my time to step up to the plate.

"My primary concern is for Bailey's wellbeing, and his weight gain. I don't know if going home is in his best interest. If I focus solely on Bailey, this is the best place he could possibly be. I think he needs the support of the TPN drip and fundamentally I want to see my child gain weight and grow."

Well, there it was. I said it. It just rolled out of my mouth and onto the table, where it met the open jaws of the teams who had endured weeks of me begging them to let us go home. Their faces aghast, clearly not expecting me to say anything close to this, I imagined them wondering where this change in desire came from.

Of course, all the team agreed as their only interest was Bailey. It always was and always would be. I wasn't the patient here, Bailey was. No matter what I wanted for our entire family, Bailey's interests had to come first. He could not gain weight on milk alone while he had a stoma; that was the simple truth.

He must stay here under the best care until they could reverse the stoma and he could show he would thrive on breastmilk once his full digestive tract was back in use. The stoma was simply too high, leaving too little tract to absorb sufficient nutrients. Team that with malabsorption of CF and it was the perfect storm.

To a sea of nodding heads, I felt empowered. I was his mother, and I was calling the shots. I was working in his best interest and I had finally seen the light. They had gently been trying to show me this whole time, but I couldn't see it until now. For now, Bailey *needs* to be here, even though I don't *want* him to be here.

Dr Crosley confirmed she couldn't do the reversal for at least another three weeks. We had done five weeks now, so what was another three anyway?

I told Kev, then went for a walk to clear my head and figure out how on earth I was to tell the boys.

How had it got to this? None of this was OK, yet here I was accepting it all and feeling like I had stopped fighting. Or had I just won the battle? I simply didn't know.

20th July

When you're in hospital with a baby, it's the small things we all take for granted that become the most precious things, big issues or problematic situations.

Bailey was almost six weeks old and I still hadn't registered his birth. Legally in the UK you have to register babies within forty-two days of their birth. Bailey was forty days old today, which meant I had to do it by 22nd July. How on earth was I meant to register the birth of a child who was constantly on a drip, and therefore could not attend the appointment?

I had spoken to the registry office a few days ago and had obtained a letter from Great Ormond Street Hospital to confirm that my son was currently their patient (not sure why I would lie about something so awful, but there we are – doing as I was told).

You also envisage it is something you'll do together as parents, but in this instance, Kev took the day off rugby to sit with Bailey, while I headed home to make Bailey's birth legal, by myself. No husband. No baby.

I had booked my appointment for the morning, so I could collect Harry and Mylo at 1:30pm for the start of their school summer holidays. First of all,

Unconditional Love

I was late leaving due to a burst stoma bag, then the trains were delayed, so I made it to the registry office with one minute to spare. Although I was aware registering Bailey's birth was important, in truth I had given it little thought.

It was me that convinced Kev to call Bailey his name, Kev being slightly hesitant at first. One C-section later, he thinks I'm amazing and that's when you strike – the easiest 'yes' you'll ever get.

However, his middle name had not been chosen and since everything had happened it hadn't been a topic we had revisited. Sat in the registry office, the lady asked me for his full name, including his middle name.

"Uh, I'm not actually sure. I'm so sorry, I'm not really with it. It's been a bit of a torrid few weeks. I'm so sorry. I think I will need to call my husband to discuss it."

I mean, truly? This poor lady must have thought I was the worst mother in the world. Not only had I rocked up flustered, without the baby and basically late, I was now unsure of my own child's name. I dread to think what she was thinking.

I duly called Kev's mobile. No answer. Damn. So I called the reception desk of Bailey's ward.

"Hi, it's Laura Barrett. Kev is there with Bailey Barrett. I'm registering Bailey's birth, but I don't know what middle name to give him. I tried to call Kev, but he isn't answering his phone. Please can you check Bailey's room and ask him to call me back if he is in there."

A slightly confused nurse duly ran the kind errand and soon enough Kev was on the phone. Clearly the catalogue of events was taking its toll on us both as he was as clueless as I.

Harry has Kev's dad's name, Mark, and Mylo has my dad's name, Michael, so where did that leave Bailey?

"Just pick a name, pick a name," my head was saying, feeling hot and flustered as the lady patiently waited.

"Thomas, let's just call him Thomas to copy your middle name, Kev. That will be fine," I said.

Kev agreed. Great, job done.

"Thomas. Just put down Thomas. It's my husband's middle name so that's fine."

The very kind, patient, somewhat perturbed lady simply said, "You do know you can't change this after today?" She was clearly very concerned with the thoughtless approach we took to naming our child.

Next question: "So what's your marriage date?"

Oh my goodness, my brain is literally mush. I'm a massive dates person and yet I simply had no idea. I sat in the chair feeling increasingly uncomfortable. I literally had no idea when Kev and I got married. I knew it was June as everyone from rugby gets married in June as it's the rugby off season, but what date? I tried to visualise the order of service we have framed in our bedroom with my bouquet. No. It's no good, I actually didn't know.

By now the lady is looking concerned. I was unsure if it was about my mental health or the fact this appointment was taking far longer than it should. Either way, I was absolutely sweating.

"Twelfth. It's the 12th June. We got married at our university chapel on 12th June. The same date we brought our son Bailey home from our local hospital following his birth. We've been married eight years."

Thank God! I think I gave all the extra information to prove my legitimacy, but she swiftly stopped me and carried on with the rest of the appointment.

The lady and I were relieved once we drew to a close and she genuinely wished me well – I hoped she meant for the baby rather than my own wellbeing.

The entire event proved how institutionalised I had become at GOSH, and how I had no mental capacity for anything other than stoma bags, Creon doses, drip bag changes and childcare arrangements. My mind was literally mush.

As planned, I collected Harry and Mylo from school and the whole village went to the common for the traditional gathering to celebrate the end of school and start of the summer holidays.

The common was heaving, parents and children turning out in their droves with picnic blankets, drinks, snacks and ball games. I had longed to be able to bring Bailey to this event, but sadly it wasn't meant to be.

By now most people knew of Bailey's situation, most just knowing he was in GOSH, but not why. I was grateful it was a sunny day so I could hide behind my sunglasses once more. I sat with my closest friends Hannah, Karen, Katie, Donna, Alex and Lisa, so I felt at ease and enjoyed seeing the boys play so nicely.

Again though, I was thankful to get home and feel safe behind closed doors. I had developed a crippling paranoia around people. It was a combination of thinking people judged me for not knowing I carry the CF gene and being so irresponsible, along with their views on leaving my newborn son. It wasn't something I wanted to do; it was something I had to do to continue being a mother to Harry and Mylo also. I wanted to scream at the top of my voice to explain why I had to leave without him and that I didn't want to. I wanted to shout from the roof tops that my heart was breaking. I felt a need to justify my actions and my presence in the village without my son.

Whether anyone judged me, or whether it was all in my head, I don't know, but I do know everyone was always lovely to me. For them, they probably didn't know whether to mention it or not, ask questions, or just leave the topic altogether. It was just awkward and I didn't want to make anyone feel uncomfortable.

The boys and I wandered home, me feeling tired and them high on sugar and socialising. I snuggled them up in bed and headed for my big empty bed, minus Kev who was spending the night at Bailey's side.

That night I went to bed without the crib next to me. I had asked Kev to move Bailey's still-empty crib into his room as it was just breaking my heart every time I came home.

Before I liked it being there as it offered hope. Now my hope had been replaced with acceptance. Acceptance that he wasn't coming home any time soon. Acceptance that his stay at GOSH would continue for many weeks to come.

The room looked empty without it there, but just as I loved Kev for leaving it there until today, I now loved him for respecting my wishes and remembering to do as I had requested amongst all his other household chores and work.

Kev is, and always has been, my rock. My best friend, confidant and one true love. It's cliché, but we met at university when I was nineteen and I have never looked at another man since.

21st July

Kev got the train back home so we could spend the day as a family of four and I could actually get to spend time with my husband. Meanwhile, Bailey was spending the day with granny.

It's fair to say Kev and I had seen very little of each other since his return to work. He was living at home and I was living at GOSH. In order to see me, he had to book a babysitter for the boys and come visit in the evenings after work.

Fridays were of course our regular evening as husband and wife, thanks to my lovely mum sitting with Bailey so I could head home. I missed Kev hugely.

Later that day I was back at GOSH, holding my little Bailey, whiling away another weekend on the eerily quiet ward.

22nd July

The boys returned for their regular Sunday visit. We went for a trip to the park and for some dinner.

I was also sure to clearly talk them through the childcare plans for them. The summer holidays bought new challenges of who could look after Harry and Mylo while Kev was at rugby and I was still in hospital.

My dream of being home for the holidays had not been realised, so now we needed weeks of childcare. It was a mix of exceptionally kind friends and family taking them out for wonderful day trips, fun-filled sleepovers and even a few days in Bournemouth on the beach with Grandad.

I had the whole summer holiday mapped out on a calendar so the boys, Kev and I knew where they were going when, with who and at what time. It was the hottest UK summer on record, with scorched grass and soaring temperatures, so their days were filled with outdoor-pool swims, splash parks, picnics, ice creams and true summer holiday vibes.

They were living the dream, and this is exactly the way I had planned it. Everything was a treat and fun – not a necessity. I didn't want them to feel like they were a burden or being passed around. I wanted them to be as unaffected by this as humanly possible, and from the excitement in their faces and glee in their eyes, it was just that.

I had also booked several online food shops to cater for their packed lunches for outings, and general dinners with Kev, so I could rest assured they had all they needed in my absence. As if all that was going on at GOSH wasn't enough for my shrivelling brain, food shops and childcare rotas was keeping me slightly in the real world.

It was a calm day and I think my final acceptance that we were here until the stoma reversal made things a bit easier. I had stopped fighting and was just going with the flow a bit more.

At 10pm that night, the nurse arrived to take some blood from Bailey's line, then she hung his overnight drip. However, the PICC line got blocked and they couldn't release it.

My heart was racing. We couldn't afford to lose the line as Bailey would require a general anaesthetic in order to get a new one put in. Time went on, but they still didn't have any joy.

It's amazing how rapidly things can change in hospitals. One moment all is calm, then the next second it's a frenzy of activity.

By midnight five people were at Bailey's bedside trying to sort the issue. Time seemed to drag on in slow motion, but finally they managed to unblock the line. However, it did mean Bailey couldn't have his overnight drip, which I wasn't happy about as tomorrow was weigh-in day and in my irrational, emotional mother head, this would make all the difference.

It also meant Bailey was unsettled all night, so we were both up all hours. How can you settle a hungry baby that you're not allowed to feed? It's no fun, I assure you.

23rd July

Given Bailey and I were awake with the larks, they weighed him at 6am and he had put on 40g.

I felt exhausted today with last night's events and such little sleep, but I spied Liana was on HDU with little Sienna, so I put Bailey in his pram and went for a walk to see her. We sat and chatted for ages and little Sienna was doing well, despite ongoing operations. They didn't have any clear idea of timeline to get home either, so we were empathetic towards each other's situation.

Later that day, I braved it back onto social media for want of a distraction, and when my Facebook showed me a 'memory' I went cold. It was the most unexpected memory; one that I didn't actually have an awareness of until today.

Back in 2016 I ran the London marathon. Several friends and family had come to cheer me on and take photos along the way. One of those photos was now staring at me in the face, like it was laughing at me.

There was me, in a pink running top at mile seventeen, proudly waving to the friendly face who took the photo. I was the only person I had ever noticed in this photo, until now. Right next to me, on my right hand side, was a man wearing a Cystic Fibrosis Trust T-shirt. My CBT friend Lisa, and I'm sure many others, would call this a cognitive bias. I, however, saw this as a sign. A sign that the universe had been trying to tell me or warn me about CF this whole time, but I had been too ignorant or arrogant, or both, to listen. I hadn't seen the signs. I hadn't wanted to see them. What else had I missed? How had I never noticed there was even a man stood next to me before? I felt sick to the bottom of my stomach.

I resolved to stop going on social media. It was not serving me at this time.

24th July

I took Bailey out for lots of fresh air today as it was such a beautiful day. I was still in thick jumpers under the hospital air con, so when I stepped outside the heat was striking. I ensured Bailey's sun parasol was up, but also gave him a few rays for some much-needed vitamin D. I hated him not having fresh air and natural daylight over this time.

Every time I stepped foot outside, the entrance area was always awash with people standing puffing on a cigarette. I wanted to scream at them to stop. I saw smoking differently now I was a mother to a child with CF. How could they damage their perfectly healthy lungs voluntarily, when my son was doing all he could to care and prolong the health of his lungs, through no fault of his own? It just didn't seem fair.

I gave the smoke-clouded crowds a wide berth and as we walked, I just thought about all the nice things we could be doing in this lovely weather with the boys off school. All the friends that were taking care of them, we could have been seeing together as days out. We had lost so much time now, and it made me feel so sad. I know we have our whole lives as a family of five, but I yearned for it to my core.

Mylo had asked me on the phone the other night when we would be coming home "properly". I just wish I could answer him, but I still have no idea. I don't want to say a date and then it changes, as that would be so cruel and unfair on my little four-year-old monkey.

I felt exceptionally sad and emotional today, so I took to my journal.

The boys adore you Bailey. They miss you and want you home. They had you home for one day and then you were gone. Whisked away from them. You three boys are meant to be together and forging your brotherly bond. I know you will still do this, and hopefully this event makes you closer rather than more distant. I know those boys will protect and care for you, as much as daddy and I. Love you xx

25ᵗʰ July

Todays' weigh-in showed a 60g gain – good, but not great.

Bailey had a slight temperature so the nurses decided to run some blood tests. The results showed a low blood haemoglobin. Consequently, murmurs of a blood transfusion resurfaced.

Dr Crosley had mentioned a blood transfusion a couple of weeks ago, but she was holding off to see how Bailey progressed. She stopped all blood tests to reduce the amount of blood being taken from Bailey to give him the best possible chance of replenishing. I loved her approach.

However, Dr Crosley was off this week and another surgeon was covering her patients. He decided he wanted to go ahead with the blood transfusion. I instantly wondered if Dr Crosley would be doing the same and wished she was here to make the final call.

For some reason I had a stigma about the blood transfusion. I desperately didn't want Bailey to have one – not for any religious or cultural reason, but more because I wanted all his blood to be his own; the blood we had made and given him. I wanted him to be completely Bailey.

I realise how ridiculous I sometimes sound in relation to certain events, but at a time of such emotion and trauma, I think things get thwarted or blown up. I didn't want my forty-five-day-old child to require a blood transfusion. Simple.

I wanted time to think about it, so I went for a walk and sat outside a nearby coffee shop in the sun. As I was sipping my tea with Bailey asleep in his pram next to me, a blood donor van pulled up on the roadside right next to us.

A sign. I took this as my decision made. Or, as Lisa would have told me, a cognitive bias.

I went back with my mind made up, but still wondered if this would be happening if Dr Crosley was here. I chatted to Kev and my mum, who both agreed it was for the best. I signed the consent form. They would perform the transfusion tomorrow.

That evening my mum and sister came in and we went out to a restaurant for dinner, taking Bailey in his pram too. We sat outside in the piazza and had some delicious food and a glass of wine. It was just what I needed after another stressful day.

As I checked my watch, it was 7:58pm. Bailey had to be put onto his drip at 8pm, but I had completely lost track of time. The nurses were going to be out looking for us at this rate thinking we had gone AWOL.

Like a naughty teenager, I ran as fast I could while pushing a pram back to the ward, leaving my mum and Jules to foot the restaurant bill. I careered onto the ward corridor hot and flustered, to several smiling nurses calling us dirty stop outs.

Mum and Jules returned to our room as they were attaching Bailey to his drip. They stayed for a while and we chatted and laughed. We laughed so loud they could hear us at the nurse's desk, with a couple of nurses coming in to check all was OK. Soon enough they were giggling with us. I've no idea exactly what we were laughing about, but we just couldn't stop, so-much-so that tears rolled down my cheeks.

Then Kev turned up for a surprise visit. We all turned to see him stood in the doorway and just laughed.

"I can hear you all from down the corridor," he said, with a smile across his face.

I never thought I would laugh like that again, and certainly not while still in here. It felt good, and I was glad that Kev was there with us too.

26th July

I try to start every day at GOSH hoping it will be a positive and happy day. But my hopes hadn't been renewed yet, and this day would be no different.

While I waited for them to get the blood ready for Bailey's transfusion, the CF dietician and surgical dietician came to see me. I was familiar with Lucy the CF dietician from previous meetings – we had worked closely together to get Bailey's Creon dose right for his milk. I hadn't met the surgical dietician before; I didn't actually know there was one until now.

They sat down and took me through all Bailey's weight stats, the optimal growth chart and various other factors. I knew it was going somewhere, but I just didn't quite know where.

They told me that they simply couldn't control Bailey's stoma output and his weight gain wasn't sufficient. He was now falling well below the line on the chart they were waving in front of me and they explained he needed to gain weight and be healthy to operate for the stoma reversal. The two ladies gently informed me that Bailey will have to go back on a drip twenty-four hours a day instead of just overnight, and his milk feeds will be reduced from 45mls to 20mls.

I couldn't believe it. I stood there aghast, unsuccessfully holding back my tears.

It all felt like such backwards steps, and also meant I couldn't take Bailey outside any more for little walks of fresh air and sunlight.

My dad was here with me. He stood behind me, but he didn't say a word. He just gently placed his hand on my shoulder and handed me a tissue. My dad was the type of man who still carried handkerchiefs in his pocket, so I was thankful it was a fresh tissue, rather than a used hanky.

I felt like life was spiralling again. It all felt so out of control. I felt like I was also the last to know or be consulted, yet Bailey was *my* child. I was now exceptionally upset, but also cross. I felt so angry. At the nurses, or the situation or simply the whole thing, I didn't know, but I was frustrated, to put it mildly.

Bailey's milk feed was due, so I walked over to the nurse's station to get a spoon. Every time I fed Bailey, I had to put some apple puree on a spoon, put the tiny Creon beads on top and give it to him before he drank his milk. Yet obviously because he was so young, the nurses had to sterilise the spoon between feeds. This meant every time I wanted to feed Bailey, I had to find a nurse who was free, and ask her for the spoon. It was an annoying, protracted affair but something I'd become used to.

However, today when I requested the spoon for Bailey's feed, they couldn't find it. Several nurses looked in the usual places, but it was nowhere to be seen. This for me, today, was the final straw. I snapped.

"How on earth do you expect me to feed my baby his milk when you can't find the spoon. This is ridiculous. This place is insane. I can't live like this anymore. I just want a spoon to feed my baby!"

I broke down in tears in the middle of the corridor, and just at that very moment, the most amazing lady caught me; Jessica.

I had met Jessica a while back now, when I was again resisting the advice and help of nurses who wanted Bailey to have a dummy. I had not given

Harry and Mylo a dummy, and so I didn't want Bailey to have one. Rightly or wrongly, I wanted to treat them the same, despite their very different starts in life. However, because he wasn't able to breast or bottle feed for so long at the beginning of his time here, he needed something to suck as it's a baby's natural reflex.

Jessica is a specialist in the neonatal world, so she gently explained why it would be best for Bailey and that I had to accept things are different this time round. We agreed to compromise on a teat of a NUK bottle, as that's the bottle the boys had used, and filled the airgap with some tissue. And that's how poor little Bailey spent his GOSH days; sucking on a tissue-filled teat.

I had seen Jessica around the ward since then and enjoyed a quick chat, but we hadn't spoken properly again until now.

I knew Jessica would understand how I was feeling as she had actually found herself in GOSH as a mother when one of her own children required medical care.

I told Jessica about the blood transfusion, the increased drip and the decreased milk. I told her about the missing spoon and my loss of control. I told her all of it, and she understood all of it entirely. She was so empathetic and it made me realise how her own challenging story from the past must help her in her job today. I pray one day I can use this trying situation to help others, but no idea quite how.

Jessica made me see that everything I was upset about today was all short lived, just to get Bailey ready for his surgery. She explained that the sooner Bailey was ready, the sooner they could operate and the sooner we could start the road to recovery and get home.

By the end of our chat we were both giggling at how silly it was, so we labelled today 'Spoon Gate'. Jessica had also had a day like mine where she had lost control once while she was here, which made me feel like I wasn't going mad.

I went back to the room, and they had obviously found the spoon because my dad was feeding Bailey his bottle of milk. I hated him seeing me so lost, but I was grateful he was there. He was present without being overbearing; he was just there and that was all I needed.

Following the Spoon Gate disaster, the nurses decided to put a microwave in the breastfeeding room so mums could sterilise their own spoons. Genius! Such a simple solution to an avoidable problem.

Bailey's blood type is O Positive. A bag of universal O Negative blood had arrived and they were due to start administering it via Bailey's PICC line. The nonchalance with which the nurses viewed blood transfusions struck me; so every day to them. I must have checked with them twenty times that Bailey could definitely have this blood type.

I've never had a blood transfusion so knew very little about them until now, however I have donated blood and I felt a pang of gratitude to whoever took the time to donate their blood to help Bailey and others. I made a mental note to always donate my blood and give back.

I held Bailey the whole time as the 45mls of blood dripped into his little body. I wondered what Bailey would have done if he could have told me his decision. Here I was making all these choices and signing all these consent forms, but it wasn't my body, it was his. What would Bailey think of my choices when he was older? He won't be able to give blood when he is old enough now he's had a blood transfusion. I have taken that choice away from him. Will he mind?

Every decision I make is for him. It would be so much easier to make these decisions if it only affected me, but it doesn't – it's his life. I have to make choices and act in what I believe to be in his best interest. I constantly doubt myself and always wonder what he would do if he was old enough to make up his own mind. I just pray that one day he won't resent or be cross for any choices I make now, and in future months and years.

Later that day Bailey's apple puree went missing, just like the spoon before it. I had to keep his puree in the hospital fridge, which like everything else, I wasn't allowed to access because it also housed other children's medicines and milk.

It was just one more thing too far. On such a challenging day, during such a traumatic time, these little things seem huge. As a parent, you've lost control of your child, so you cling on to anything you can control. You know their feed times, as you live by the clock, willing away the time, knowing that's one less day in this place. So when you can't do the one thing you feel you're in control of, it tips you over the edge.

I couldn't access his puree and I couldn't sterilise his spoon, yet I was his mother. And the people who were meant to be helping me, had indeed lost both the puree and the spoon in one day.

I was so irate when they couldn't find the apple puree that I walked out of the hospital with Bailey, and took us for dinner and drinks in the warmth of the summer's evening. Bailey wouldn't be able to go out for a while after today once he was back on his drip twenty-four hours a day, so I wanted to make the most of it.

When I returned, his drip went up, and he was tied to the inside of these walls yet again.

When would it all settle down? I journaled to calm myself.

I'm so sorry Bailey. I'm so sorry for this awful start in life. I'm so sorry for giving you the CF gene that has led to all of this. If I could take it all from you, I would. Please forgive me, darling boy.

I just wish I knew what you wanted. I wish you could tell me the choices you would make as a grown man. I am making such important decisions that impact you, but it's not my body. I hope one day, when you understand everything, that you feel I made the right choices – the decisions you would have made had you been able to understand and talk. You are so small, yet you've been through so much, and you power on through. I am so very privileged to be your mummy xx

27th July

Today was Bailey's first day back on the drip full time so he was confined to his room and I wasn't eager to leave him, so I stayed there too.

The CF psychologist came to see how we were doing. I enjoyed our chats as she did really understand some of my feelings, but I also felt that she thought if Dr Crosley was here, things might be unravelling themselves slightly differently. I still wondered what Dr Crosley was going to say about the blood transfusion upon her return. Maybe I should have resisted until she was back?

My mum was looking after the boys at home, so the three of them travelled on the train into London, and Mum sat with Bailey while the boys and I headed back home on the train. Kev was away at a rugby sevens tournament and I wanted to spend a couple of the days with the boys during the school summer holidays.

Of course, I didn't want to leave Bailey, but deep down I knew it would do me good after recent events.

The boys made me laugh so much on the train home – their company was so longed for and I treasured each moment with them.

28th July

Today I took the boys to the kite festival, Bailey, which you would have loved. As we were staring up at the beautiful blue sky watching a myriad of kites swooping and soaring, I felt so sad you weren't with us.

The boys wanted to buy you a mini kite for when you get home. They also picked a dandelion and we blew it and we all wished you were coming home soon.

We got the water slide out in the garden so they could have some slippery fun. It has two lanes, but the boys said we need to get a new one that has three lanes so you can have your own lane too.

They think about you all the time, and talk of you often. Their love for you is as unconditional as mine and daddy's, and it melts my heart.

I admit it feels so nice to be home, in my own bed and taking a long, hot soak in the bath. It makes me want to get you home all the more. You will love it here Bailey; bathing with your brothers and snuggling up in your room with all your teddies and fresh, soft carpet. Your room is all ready for you – you just aren't ready quite yet. Soon my baby xx

29th July

Kev, the boys and I all drove into London to see Bailey and relieve my mum of her granny duties. They had their usual cuddles and playtime and then headed home, leaving me here for another week of hospital life.

Soon after, the weekend doctor came by to inform me they were going to reduce Bailey's milk to 10mls per feed as the stoma output was too high.

I felt furious. This all seemed so ridiculous. Nothing seemed to be working. A tiny 10mls wasn't going to do much. How on earth could we get this stoma to work properly? It felt like a losing battle. I just wanted this stoma reversed as soon as we could, then we would get a proper gauge as to how Bailey's body could perform with a full digestive tract in use. I wanted Dr Crosley back.

Bailey was looking well, with more colour to his face compared to his white complexion of weeks ago. He looked so content and perfect, and I began to worry there was something else at play – that something else was going on in his little body other than cystic fibrosis.

Now we knew that we were at GOSH until the stoma reversal, it felt like we were just biding our time until they could perform this procedure. In short, it felt like we were sitting ducks, just wasting life.

When I was at home, I had packed my running gear. I am a lover of running, and knew it was time to find a way to cope during this situation. Running was my go-to; my release. If we weren't going home for a while, then I would bring a touch of my home lifestyle to this clinical world.

That evening, I put on my running kit, slipped on my trainers and went out to pound the streets of London. It was a damp, humid dusk run, but it felt good. I took it easy given I hadn't run throughout my pregnancy with Bailey, and I was still healing from my C section, but it felt reviving to get back out there.

I was determined that as Bailey got stronger, so would I. As I grew fitter, so Bailey's condition would improve. We would do this together!

30th July

A weight gain this morning, taking Bailey up to 7.6lbs. A positive start.

Afterwards we had to take Bailey down to X-ray to check his bowel had completely cleared before they could operate to reverse the stoma.

We were in this X-ray room on the second day after we first arrived to try to wash out the stuck meconium. It felt like a lifetime ago – so much had happened since then.

Plenty of visitors arrived today too, in the form of James (Amy's husband, who resembled the BFG as he is super tall, but so gentle), Kev's sister Clair and my sister Jules. Everyone was so kind taking the time out of their busy lives to check-in on us. Our frequent guests really kept us going and I was thankful Bailey was used to other people's voices and being held.

Later that day, Dr Crosley strode back into the room after her time off. I've never been more delighted to see her. I could have hugged her, but knew that went well over the lines of her professional part in this journey. I just felt so comforted by her presence. She knew our journey and Bailey so well that is felt reassuring.

She didn't really talk about the blood transfusion. Inside I was longing to ask her if she would have done the same, but professionally she couldn't say no, so I kept quiet.

She did however wonder if the daily antibiotic Bailey was taking for his CF, Flucloxacillin, was making the stoma output high. She advised she would temporarily stop the antibiotic and inform the CF team, and hoped this would help.

"We will operate to perform the stoma reversal on Tuesday 7th August." And just like that, the date was set. That was just eight days away!

Finally, a goal, a target to work towards, and once that was done, it was just a case of recovering from the operation, showing Bailey could gain weight on breastmilk alone and then we would be out of here. The rest of the CF management could be done from home.

It was the stoma that was the reason we were still here, so once the stoma was gone, that would be that. I wished they'd never done the stoma and then we would have been home ages ago, but I kept telling myself they did what they had to do at that present moment, not having all the facts and genetic information we now have. But goodness, I hated that stoma and the impact it had.

With the date set, it finally felt like there was light at the end of this very long tunnel. For the first time, I felt a ray of hope and touch of excitement.

31st July

My friend Alex kindly brought in the crazy big boys today. It was lovely to see them mid-week while they were off school as it really broke up the week-long stretches we had been doing.

After they'd left, the cleaner came round to do Bailey's room. These cleaners came three to four times a week to wash the floors, rub down the beds and tables, top up the hand sanitiser, refill the paper towel dispenser and generally ensure everything was sterile and free from germs.

I had gained a huge appreciation for these staff members, seeing them work daily on the ward and realising the importance their role played in here. Neonatal babies, sick children, little ones with cystic fibrosis – all these patients need clean environments to avoid infections that could set them back in their progress or indeed delay procedures.

Their role meant that the top specialists always had clean hands and equipment needed to fulfil their work. They were such an important cog in a very big wheel, but one that often gets overlooked or underappreciated.

I got to know all the cleaners as we'd been here so long, and we often had little chats. They commented on Bailey each time, and said he was looking much better now. It made me realise how much they must see and hear while going about their daily work, without anyone noticing quite what they are privy to.

It's funny sometimes how by sitting still for long enough, you can learn to appreciate things you otherwise didn't see before.

1st August

A new month and we were still here. I just couldn't believe that we had been here since June – it still all felt so surreal.

Bailey underwent a biopsy today on his bowel just to double check for any potential abnormalities before they reversed the stoma. They had taken a biopsy during his first surgery to check for Hirschsprung disease, but it had come back inconclusive, so they wanted to repeat it to rule it out. They would have the results in a day or two.

The nurse carried Bailey to the treatment room on the ward, where they took three little samples using a tube up his bottom. The nurses returned my baby to me naked and wrapped in a towel, because there was blood on his baby grow.

As I rinsed Bailey's blood-stained clothes in the sink, a tear rolled down my eye as I watched the red liquid whirl down the plughole. I felt so sad that Bailey had endured so much so young, and I couldn't find peace in accepting all that had happened. It wasn't a 'why me?', because in my mind nobody should have to go through this ever again, but it was just an utter disbelief.

I dressed Bailey into a new grow and wrapped him up as snug as a bug to warm him up.

Our room was a hive of activity with guests including Kerri and Emily from Kev's rugby, my dad's partner Margaret, my university friend Bex and my mum and Kev. So many amazing friends and family, and so much love to see us through.

2nd August

Today was due to be a quiet day with just one visitor, MJ who I knew from Saracens rugby. MJ also used to be a nurse, so she was familiar with this medical world.

However, while she was with us MJ noticed a tear in Bailey's PICC line. At first I wasn't too worried, but when I looked closer she was absolutely right and it really didn't look too good – like it might split entirely at any moment.

I had forged a strong rapport with a nurse called Bethany, who often cared for Bailey on her shift. She was working today, so I showed her the area of PICC line we were worried about. She thought it would be fine, but called the CVAC specialist just to be sure.

Amy from the CVAC team arrived and confirmed that the line was broken, mainly due to the fact it hadn't been dressed properly. She felt confident she could fix it, but it meant Bailey couldn't have his TPN drip until then.

I felt so distressed – not only was this yet another hurdle we had to overcome in amongst everything else, but it was another night without TPN before weigh-in day. If all decisions were based on Bailey's weight, this wasn't going to work in his favour and I couldn't bear it if his surgery was postponed.

They wanted to cannulate Bailey overnight so he could have an IV drip. Having seen how many cannulas he had endured weeks ago and how tricky he seemed to be to cannulate, I advised the doctor that he might need the specialist to perform the procedure.

Nobody listened however, and the doctor tried to find a vein for the cannula. As predicted, he could not do it, so he called for the specialist as I had first recommended. I knew my son, and I felt very unheard.

Thankfully the specialist was successful on her first attempt. The whole event transported me back six or seven weeks, and I couldn't believe we were back here again.

Later Amy returned to fix the PICC line. It was intricate, painstaking work, and they needed Bailey to be very still, and everything had to be completely sterile. They performed the procedure in his room, so I sat watching with baited breath. It took so long, and they were asking so much of Bailey to be so still while they worked, and my heart just bled for him. My poor little boy.

After what felt like hours, Amy confirmed she had fixed the line, but was unsure how much longer it would last. It had to be dressed a specific way, so she had attached it to his torso with clear sticky patches, rather than the top of Bailey's arm where it had been. His whole tiny body was literally covered in large see-through patches, his skin all crinkled underneath.

All these sticky patches were making Bailey's delicate, new skin so dry and sore. I just wanted to rip them all off, soak him in a lovely bubble bath and hug him in a soft, white towel, all while free from tubes. That day would have to wait for now though.

I found the whole ordeal today so stressful. Once the team left the room, I just sat down in the chair next to Bailey and sobbed my heart out. It was such a rollercoaster of a journey that we seemed to be on, and there didn't seem to be any let up. There was always another obstacle or upset to overcome. It didn't ever seem to quite go our way in here. Perhaps this is how it was in here, or maybe it was just Bailey's journey?

I had called Kev totally distraught and exhausted from the day's events. I was running out of steam – how long could this go on for? And how long could I carry on living like this?

I collapsed in the chair for the evening, exhausted, upset and not hungry for any dinner. I left the TV off and just allowed myself to get lost in my thoughts and tears.

A while later, about 9pm there was a gentle tap at the door. It slowly opened and there, standing strong and handsome, was Kev. The only person in the world that I wanted to let in at this moment. Just as I was completely falling apart, there he was to catch me. This was the second occasion where Kev read the situation just right and knew exactly what I needed; him.

I was so delighted to see him. He held me so tight while I cried into his strong body, and then he held Bailey while I made us a cup of peppermint tea. I love this man so much and am so lucky to have him as my partner in life.

Kev left for his long drive home, late night and early start, while I tried to comfort a very hungry, discontent Bailey. We spent the whole night together, pacing the room, trying to comfort a hungry baby without any food.

3rd August

Amy from the CVAC team poked her cheery face around the corner this morning to check Bailey's line was OK. She was happy with her work and confirmed it was now fine to use, so Bailey could return to his TPN, which hopefully would sedate his hunger and upset, pronto.

Bailey's weight went from 7.8lbs to 7.7lbs, so a loss, but hardly. Equally though, not a gain, despite twenty-four-hour TPN.

My friend Katy visited today, travelling down from Sheffield to see us. Our friendship dates all the way back to school, so it was wonderful to have such a familiar face after yesterday's troubling day. It was so amazing to see her, and we laughed, cried and chatted about everything and anything.

Recently I was finding that a lot of staff members I had built relationships with and who knew Bailey's story well were starting to move on, which was making me feel a bit wobbly.

A lovely Irish nurse called Kathleen had left for another hospital, and two men on Dr Crosley's team had also moved on. I really missed seeing Islam and Dr David, especially Dr David as he was always so lovey to Bailey. He really had a natural rapport with children, which felt less clinical and stilted.

I felt shattered this evening after such a disturbed night last night, but then a little head appeared at our door

"Can I come in?"

It was Kathleen, who had returned to do a bank shift before she started her new job. She was meant to be taking some time off beforehand, but there was obviously no keeping her away.

She was always so cheery and seemed to have such a genuine care for little Bailey. She kindly offered to do Bailey's night feeds so I could sleep. Trusting Kathleen and knowing her as I did, in a rare acceptance of help, I took up her very kind offer so I could catch up on some sleep.

It felt strange to me having the option to 'duck out' of the night feeds. As a mother of a newborn, you're meant to be tired. And as a mother who has breastfed the boys, I'd been used to around ten months of broken sleep per child.

This time round, to have people offer to do the night feeds felt so alien, and I hated the fact that I could choose to not fulfil what I saw as my only remaining role, so I never accepted. Except for tonight. Tonight I was exhausted, and I had a nurse caring for Bailey who I knew well.

I also knew that these were exceptional circumstances, and my fatigue now was very different to that of a mother to a newborn who was up in the night for feeds. I had to get sleep to be able to cope with whatever was hurled at us next. I had to be strong for Bailey and I. Sleep was pivotal to my wellbeing in these times.

4th August
Daddy is coming to look after you today Bailey, so I can go home to see the big boys. I know you are going to have such a great time with him. I'll miss you and your lovely smile, but I will be back tomorrow with Harry and Mylo for more big brother cuddles.

Seeing you smile for the first time today Bailey was simply magical. I sometimes wonder if being in here and enduring all you have will hold you back slightly in your baby development stages, but clearly not. There you are, finding a reason to smile amidst the toughest of starts in life. You truly are our inspiration.

5th August

Kev has been at Saracens rugby club for seven years, and we are exceptionally fortunate to be part of a rugby family. Although Kev had continued to go to work throughout this time, they were of course aware of what was going on his personal life. They would kindly check-in on him and also let him leave early if things were going on at the hospital.

However, today they were treating us to something so very special. They had booked Kev, Harry, Mylo and I into a hotel around the corner from GOSH for the night, and then tomorrow we were going on a boat trip down the River Thames.

Lucy, who had kindly organised the whole outing for us, blew me away with her kindness and understanding. She had checked what date would work based on what was going on with Bailey, and she had chosen a hotel so close to GOSH that we could get back quickly should we need.

My dear mum duly sat with Bailey so I could go and enjoy the experience, reassured by her presence by Bailey's bedside. The nurses and doctors now knew my mum as well as they knew Kev and me.

When we got to our hotel room, the boys were showered with gifts; hampers of sweets, Hamley's vouchers and teddy bears awaited them. They loved the novelty of room service, so they both ordered some dinner and afterwards we went down to the hotel bar for a drink to toast Bailey's eight-week birthday. I only wished he could have been here to join in his toast.

6th August

Harry and Mylo deserved this special day. They had been so good this whole time, never complaining, accepting what was before them and always being so kind to Bailey. It always astounded me how they never resented him for pulling me away from them. Their love for him was unquestionable. I had missed their fun-filled company so very much over this time, and I was truly relishing spending this special time with them.

The boys lavished in the hotel buffet breakfast and then we went for a morning swim in the hotel pool. Both Harry and Mylo were adamant they wanted to pop to the hospital to see Bailey before their boat trip, so off we went to give Bailey a little good morning kiss.

Afterwards, we headed towards the River Thames to board our boat for our excursion. It was the most beautiful sunny day, so we were in luck. We all put on life jackets and climbed aboard.

This was no leisurely cruise down the Thames. Oh no, this was a speed boat variety, which whizzed and splashed all the way along. The speed was thrilling and the G-force so strong. I could barely lift my head to see if Harry and Mylo were enjoying it – from their squeals it seemed one was, while the other wasn't so sure.

As we neared the Thames barrier, the boat slowed to talk us through some of the landmarks, then turned around to make its return leg back to the jetty.

Feeling the sun and the (very) fresh air on my face, mixed with the upbeat music played by the boat, I began to cry. For all that happened, for the time and memories lost and for all the challenges that were to come; surgery and life with cystic fibrosis.

Sometimes I think I was so caught up in life at GOSH that I rarely thought about what life would be like once we got home. I was desperate to get home, but had I really given it any thought at all in terms of Bailey's care?

I don't think I had, but perhaps I didn't have the energy to think about all that just yet. Or perhaps it just felt so far away that my mind couldn't go that far ahead.

As the boat pulled slowly into the jetty, the wind had fortunately swept away my tears; I didn't want anything to ruin Harry and Mylo's day.

Windswept, with sea legs and swearing blind they were never going on that thing again, the boys stepped onto dry land, excited for the next event on their schedule; lunch.

A table had been booked for us at Duck and Waffle – a top London restaurant on the fortieth floor, giving amazing views across London. The boys yawned to pop their ears as the lift zoomed up so high. We walked around the perimeter to take in the views and then sat down for a delicious meal.

Next stop was Hamley's to spend their voucher from their surprise hampers. Without any prompt, they decided to get one thing each, and a little gift for Bailey. I was so utterly proud to be their mummy. They just amazed me at every step of this journey. They included Bailey in all they did now, even though they hadn't really lived with him yet. My heart swelled with love for my handsome duo.

Harry chose an air hockey set while Mylo chose a swimming squid for bath time, and they agreed on a musical Noah's Ark for their baby brother.

I knew they had enjoyed the most special day and that it probably felt like the first normal one in a while, with the four of us together enjoying ourselves. I hoped the happy day we experienced signalled that we were out of the worst of it, and that it would be plain sailing and homeward bound from here on.

The boys and Kev now needed to get the train home, and I needed to get back to Great Ormond Street Hospital as I knew Dr Crosley would soon be coming round to the ward.

I hated leaving my big boys. You would think it becomes easier each time, but it doesn't. The opposite in fact; the longer this went on and the longer we were apart, the deeper the pain.

I held those boys so tight I am surprised they could breathe. I didn't want to let go. Amongst the bustle of these busy London streets was a moment of stillness between a mother and her two sons, acknowledging all they had stood up to and an outpouring of love and pride beyond measure.

I released them and watched them both bounce along, each holding hands with Kev so as not to get separated. I stayed watching them walk away until I physically couldn't see them anymore, then turned to walk back into the four walls of Bailey's room.

I filled Mum in on the day's events and as we were ooing and aahing over my photos, The Legend entered with her entourage. I was presented with the consent forms for Bailey's surgery tomorrow, which I eagerly signed like I was signing us out of here.

"I hope you had a nice day."

This was the first non-clinical thing Dr Crosley had really ever said to me. I wondered if she knew that I had been riding a speedboat full pelt down the River Thames the day before my son underwent surgery? Hardly appropriate behaviour. Yet there was an ever-so-slight smile on her face, and almost a mutual feeling of delight that we had finally reached the point of Bailey's stoma reversal. It has been some journey.

My goodness though, I would love to get inside her head and know what she thinks about this whole journey we've been on together; the first operation, the stoma issues, if she always thought it was CF right from the beginning.

Claire from the CF team came in later to chat to me. I enjoyed our time together, and she was another one I would love to be able to read better. She had been involved from the start and just as with Dr Crosley, every time she met me I had another barrage of questions. My main one for Claire was still 'because of 'X' does this mean it's a bad case of CF?'. This question still ravaged my brain daily, looking for anything to help me know what Bailey's case was like, but for now nobody knew. When would they know?

Having spent some time with both Dr Crosley and Claire today, I had a feeling that things were nearing the end. It felt as if everyone knew this stoma reversal would change everything, and we would be drawing a close on our stay here at GOSH. I so hoped my feelings were right.

I went for a run before my mum left as I thought the fitter I got, the more Bailey would thrive. My positive energy would give him positive energy. I knew tomorrow would be a tough day, especially in comparison to today's antics, so I wanted to prepare myself as much as I could. A run was the perfect end to this day.

7th August – Surgery day

The day had finally arrived; the day to reverse Bailey's stoma and hopefully start a road of weight gain towards home.

Of course I didn't want Bailey to need to have another surgery, but it felt different this time. Everyone was more in the know, I trusted Dr Crosley implicitly and it felt like this would be Bailey's turning point.

Kev arrived just before Bailey was taken down, and was greeted with huge big smiles from our little boy in his oversized theatre gown.

This time I was able to take Bailey down to theatre, showing I had grown in strength during this experience. Kev and I left Bailey and went for a coffee, both feeling positive. Two hours later, we were called to collect Bailey from recovery. We were met with a sleepy little baby, wrapped up warm and on a heated mattress.

When we arrived back on the ward Bailey was quite uncomfortable, so they gave him some morphine. I was so worried they would give him too much again like last time, but I kept reminding myself they knew what they were doing. Plus, he was bigger now too compared to the little seven-day-old baby who last went under the knife.

I checked Bailey's wound and I admit that it was lovely not to see the stoma, but instead a little tummy with a dressing on it. The wound from his previous operation had healed so well that I could hardly see it – such impressive work these surgeons do, and how clever little bodies are at repairing so beautifully.

The dose of morphine worked, and Bailey settled and simply slept. I loved to think of him sleeping and healing and growing – getting all his strength to come home to his big brothers at long last. I felt so much more positive now. I felt certain we were finally on the right path. I was glad today had come. And gone.

8th August

After a settled night's sleep, Dr Crosley came to check how Bailey was recovering, and was very pleased with his progress.

Following my cleared blood test at St Guys and Thomas, today the gentleman came to collect my homemade, gold top collection of milk filling the ward freezers. Aptly, this timed with World Breastfeeding Week. I think the nurses were as delighted to give it to him as he was to take it to the little neonates.

It felt so rewarding that something good for others would come out of our challenging time and my ability to express copious amounts of the white liquid. If Bailey couldn't have it, at least other little babies could. There were one hundred and fifty bottles donated in total, and I kept some back in one freezer drawer, just in case Bailey would need them.

Later that evening, I noticed Bailey's tummy was hard, swollen and distended again, like it was when we first arrived at GOSH with his blocked bowel. A sick feeling swam over me, wondering it there may be another blockage causing this. Perhaps he didn't only have CF?

I fretfully showed the nurse, who agreed it didn't look quite right. Soon the on-call registrar was in Bailey's room and confirmed he felt it all looked normal, but would check again in the morning.

I felt so on edge something was going to go wrong and set Bailey back. In my mind this had to be the point at which he thrived forwards. I was frightened something else was going to happen to derail our path home.

9th August

Today was the most monumental day – Bailey's first poo! After eight weeks of life, Bailey finally showed his bottom worked perfectly well. It's crazy to think how excited you can get by a poo, but I literally ran out of our room and told all the nurses at their desk.

The stool did have a lot of the thick, black meconium, which worried me slightly. However, Dr Crosley confirmed that this would soon pass. She also checked his tummy, which was much more deflated now a dose of wind and faeces had passed through. Things were looking good. Come on baby boy!

10th August

Three poos down and still tar-like meconium was coming out of Bailey's bottom. The Legend arrived and suggested the best thing to help it pass would be some milk, starting on 10mls every two hours. I was ecstatic – poo and milk all in less than twenty-four hours.

Before Dr Crosley left the room she informed me that she would be off next week, and so she said goodbye to us today in case we weren't here when she returned.

Oh. My. Goodness. She actually thinks there's a chance we might not be here when she gets back from her holiday. I couldn't believe how quickly things seemed to be moving. I knew getting rid of the stoma would be a turning point, but this was more than I ever imagined.

Trying to contain my sheer delight at this possibility, I thanked her infinitely for all her help, care and understanding over these past couple of months.

I now had Friday 17th August in my head as our date to go home, which was when Harry and Mylo were due to return from Bournemouth with my dad.

11th August

Today you were allowed 20mls of milk every two hours. You lapped up every last bit. You are doing so well Bailey – I am in awe of you and so very proud.

Today I put the radio on for the first time, and we had a little dance together. It made me wonder why I hadn't done this before, but I guess until now it hadn't been the right time.

You smiled away as we had a little boogie. It felt like the first time we had really enjoyed each other and had some fun.

I utterly adore you, Bailey xx

12th August

The whole time we were in Great Ormond Street Hospital it was like a roller coaster; good days, followed by bad days, followed by good days, and so on. The only thing was, unlike a roller coaster where you can see the track, on this ride you didn't know when the ups and downs were coming, so the downs hit you like a curve ball you never saw.

The weekend doctors were on, so you often had someone you weren't familiar with. Today it was a female doctor I'd never met before. She entered our room to inform me that Bailey was now pooing too much and we had to reduce his milk.

You honestly couldn't make it up. First, the child can't poo at all, and now he's pooing too much. I felt like he was a performing monkey.

I knew that all we simply had to do was increase Bailey's Creon dose to aid his absorption, which would then reduce his stool frequency. This is exactly what the CF dietician had taught me.

However, when I told the doctor this, she would not listen. I had been educated on CF and how to manage Creon, but here I was as Bailey's mother and I wasn't being heard or listened it, and it was infuriating.

With cystic fibrosis, it's a fine balancing act, especially to begin with. Different people will require different levels of Creon for their food (or in this case, milk) intake. If they don't have enough Creon, there's malabsorption and their losses are too high. Increase the Creon, and hey presto, absorption improves and losses reduce.

Given we were only at the beginning of working out how much Creon Bailey needed now he had a full working digestive tract, it was a case of trial and error, evolving his doses as we go.

I really felt that this doctor was going to cause a setback in Bailey's progress. I knew I couldn't speak to the CF dietician on a Sunday, so there was nothing I could do.

It sounds ridiculous that I was feeling so frustrated and cross given we are talking about such a small amount of milk, but it doesn't feel like that in the moment as every tiny little step counts. Plus, I knew that if we were managing

Bailey's CF from home, I would be in control of his Creon and would be able to make the decision, as his mother, to increase his Creon based on stool irregularities.

I'm ashamed to say, that this is another day I totally lost my control while in this hospital. I was so irate, that I put on my running kit and set out for the streets of London to de-stress. I ran further than I had run on the last occasions, and then headed down to the Thames where I stood looking out at the London Eye, tears streaming down my face.

I wanted to take my baby home and regain control as his mother. I wanted every single nurse and doctor to finally leave him alone and let us be. I feel awful for saying it, as they were there to help him, but it's how I felt in its rawest form.

I felt a pang of shame that I hadn't been the best version of myself throughout my time at GOSH, clearly shedding myself in quite a poor light. I'm usually polite, kind and understanding, but in here I had been anything but those things. It was as if I was a different person. I wondered if I would ever be the old me again, or if that person was now lost and this new Laura #2 was here to stay? I hoped not.

I ran back to the hospital, feeling much calmer. I took the lift up to Bailey's ward and when the doors opened, there stood the doctor I had been cross with.

"Oh, you've been running. I'm sure that helped," she said.

"It did, thank you. I am sorry about earlier; it's just been a tough couple of months."

She nodded, understandingly, and entered the lift, while I went back to Bailey's room for some cuddles and his tiny amount of milk.

13th August

I called Lucy, the CF dietician, very first thing this morning to discuss the Creon versus milk situation. I was like a dog with a bone as I knew once we had confirmation, we could increase Creon and continue with Bailey's milk allowance. On hearing how upset I was, she said she would come down to talk in person.

I told Lucy all about yesterday's situation and how I had suggested we simply increase the Creon. Lucy confirmed I was right and that she had even written in Bailey's notes that we could increase Creon dose if required.

I was fuming. Why had that doctor not read the notes?

Later that day I bumped into the doctor on the ward, and admit to exchanging a few cross words with her. How had she not seen Lucy's notes? I felt it was totally incompetent on her part, and had caused a lot of upset for me and deprived Bailey of his much-needed milk. Dr Crosley's covering doctor arrived and he duly put Bailey up to 30mls of milk.

In the afternoon the CF psychologist Sarah knocked on our door. I was delighted to see her, but slightly concerned that Lucy or the ward nurses had called her to advise she pay me a visit. I dread to think what they must all be thinking about my state after my recent antics.

Perhaps I was finally losing it, but actually I think it's the opposite. I believe that because I am growing stronger and also becoming more confident in my knowledge of cystic fibrosis and becoming more familiar with how Bailey's body works, that I am feeling more frustrated that I am not in control.

I am unable to do anything. His milk has to be measured for me, as do his meds. I am not allowed in the fridge they store it in and I am not able to take my own expressed milk to the freezer. I have to ask the nurse to do everything for me.

Before, when I was on my knees, that was most helpful and just what I needed, but now I want to be doing it. I want to care for my baby.

I explained all this to Sarah, who agreed that it shows I am ready to go home and manage Bailey's life with cystic fibrosis by myself. Of course, although I would be alone at home, I would always have the CF team who I could call for advice, but ultimately, I wanted to take the reins now. I was ready.

Kev visited in the evening and fed Bailey his little bottle of milk – he looked totally smitten.

14th August

Up to 40mls of milk today, and so we increased Creon slightly. All looking so positive now!

15th August

And on to 35mls of milk every two hours. That is classed as a 'full feed', so Bailey no longer needs his drip. Such a huge stepping stone.

Kev's lovely mum visited today, as did Kev, so the three of us took drip-free Bailey out for a walk and a cuppa. Oh to get him in the fresh air. It felt like such a special and positive day.

16th August

A return to full breastfeeding today – it's like we are having a sprint finish. Everyone has started talking about us going home on Saturday. They are starting to get prescriptions ready for us to take home as Bailey will still require all his usual cystic fibrosis medications, including Creon, sodium chloride, multivitamin, vitamin E and Flucloxacillin, when he starts taking it again.

In truth, the thought of going home is exceptionally overwhelming all of a sudden. Knowing what to give of which and how much, doing physio, managing CF and being mum to three boys.

I hadn't done that yet – be a mum to three boys on my own. The days after Bailey's birth were spent with Kev and Mum there, and since then I had either been with Bailey, or Harry and Mylo, but never all three by myself. I hadn't really thought about that until today. Plus, with Kev and Mum back at work, there weren't going to be many spare hands like there would have been back in June had we not come in here.

I tried to push my thoughts and concerns to the back of my mind. I had begged Dr Crosley almost every day to help us get home as soon as possible, so how could I now almost fear it? Or had I become so institutionalised in here?

Specialists kept coming in and giving me more information, lots of Dr Crosley's team visited with more information, and various people from the CF team also popped in and out. There was clearly a lot to organise and my mind was spinning.

What if I get it wrong? What if I give him too much of this? How am I going to do physio before the school run? I wonder who I call if I need to urgently come back in?

Try as I might to stop these questions and worries from surfacing, they were taking over my thoughts.

I am almost embarrassed to admit it, but the idea crossed my mind to delay Bailey's discharge until Monday when Dr Crosley was back. I suppose she had become my safety net, but I was also severely lacking in confidence as to how to care for this child without some sort of medical specialist on tap.

Deep down, I knew I would never do that because whenever we go home my worries will be the same. I had to brave the big wide world soon, build my confidence and drown in the reality of being a mum of three little people.

17th August

Weigh-in day arrived and Bailey had gained a little weight, which made me feel confident in our departure tomorrow.

The wonderful Amy from CVAC came to take out Bailey's PICC line. This really felt like his discharge was cemented; we were actually doing this. I was pleased it was Amy too as it felt like a circular end to the PICC line.

She sent me out the room for the procedure, so I went and sat with a cup of tea and my thoughts in the kitchen area.

I looked back over this whole journey, all that had happened in here and all Bailey had been through. Everyone who had visited us and all the faces I had met along the way, both staff and other mums on the ward.

Liana was still here as Sienna was awaiting her final operation, before she too could soon go home. I would miss our bedside catch ups, but with Liana living so nearby at home, I felt confident we would keep in touch. Having someone who had shared a journey like this with you was most special.

I wrote cards for various nurses who played such important roles in our journey, and I wrote one for Dr Crosley and asked the nurse to put it in her pigeon hole for when she returned. I hope she received it.

When I returned to the room, Bailey was naked and tube free, but his skin was red raw from where the patches had been and his arm was covered in blood from the exit point of the PICC. Yet it still looked so amazing to see Bailey without even one tube. He looked so beautiful.

A nurse arrived with some wipes to clean his arm, and we chatted.

'My mum is visiting tonight. Shame we can't go today really and then she could drive us home.'

This causal comment lead to the most exciting response.

"Well, I'm sure you can go home tonight if it's easier. No point staying another night if you don't need to."

Just like that. Like it was no big deal. Like it was something I could have requested at any point throughout these whole nine weeks. Nine weeks to the day, and all of a sudden, we were set free. That's honestly how it felt; like we were being freed into the big wide word.

It took a while to get my head around, but I promptly called Mum to work out the logistics of this. You would think it would be easy to leave hospital, but it wasn't. The logistics reminded me of when we had to come into GOSH from our local hospital and all the planning involved. I had three full, heavy bags, Bailey's pram, no car seat, a huge bag of medications and then of course, the little man himself.

The boys were in Bournemouth with my dad, and Kev was currently driving to collect them to bring them home. Bailey's car seat was still in Kev's car, so Mum couldn't drive us home.

Instead, we loaded up Mum's car with all our bags, and Bailey and I took the train home. It made me laugh that we had been on this life-changing ordeal, and now I was simply catching a train home. It just felt so ordinary and understated, but equally perfect – just myself and Bailey, and finally a normal situation.

When I walked out of the hospital doors, it was the strangest sensation. There was relief, of course, mixed with overwhelm for having to do all his care myself. Then there was sadness. Sadness that we ever had to enter the world of Great Ormond Street Hospital, and sadness that this wouldn't be the last time we came here.

I knew GOSH was now a huge part of Bailey's life, and therefore our family life, as he would be back here regularly for appointments and treatments. I wished that wasn't the case for him, but we had got to this point and I had to embrace the positives; we were going home to our boys.

I took a taxi from the station to the house and met my mum there, so she could drop off all our baggage. I settled Bailey into his crib, then Mum and I sat down for a drink. Shortly after, Kev arrived home with the boys asleep in the back of the car. I carried each one to their beds, and snuggled them in. They had absolutely no idea Bailey and I were home, so it was going to be the most amazing surprise when they woke up in the morning.

I finally went to bed with Bailey's crib next to my bed, with him snuggled warm and safe inside. My dream of all five of us being home had finally been realised, and while I knew we still had a long journey ahead, I relished in this moment. Welcome home Bailey, you little fighter.

18th August

The moment the boys entered our bedroom and saw Bailey in his crib brought tears to my eyes. I've never seen elation in their faces like it before, nor since. It was unadulterated happiness.

They bounded into our bed, arms outstretched to embrace me. Their hugs were everything I had been waiting for, and more. They excitedly held Bailey in bed, and they decided they all had to wear blue today to celebrate his first day back home.

So with everyone clad in blue hues, we headed out for a walk, Harry and Mylo taking it in turns to push Bailey's pram to the common. We did Bailey's physio together as a family, me bouncing him on a large exercise ball with a PEP mask, while the boys bounced around the room to music.

Kev decorated our kitchen blackboard with a sign that read 'Welcome home baby Bailey' and the boys finally got their long-awaited bath altogether. It was a magical day and the very moments I had longed for while apart. Plus, we still had three weeks of the school summer holidays to enjoy.

Yet my fears and overwhelm I felt on leaving GOSH were founded, as the days and weeks that followed were harder than I ever imagined.

Visit www.laura-barrett.co.uk to view a gallery of photos of Bailey's journey from Great Ormond Street Hospital to today.

HOME

Our new life at home began positively and excitedly. I arranged a homecoming gathering on our village common, with all our family and friends who had helped us so much over the past few months. The sun shone for Bailey that day like never before and everyone drank and laughed while the children played and Bailey was cuddled.

We also received the most special gift. I had previously mentioned to my friends Amy and Sarah about all the Bailey signs in the Ciao Bella restaurant next door to GOSH. Befuddled, I had researched into it to learn that the world-renowned famous photographer David Bailey lived and worked nearby, and this was a selection of his work.

In a gesture of unimaginable kindness and thoughtfulness, the girls had bought me the book *Bailey's Stardust*. It had the most striking multi-coloured cover with a star on the front, and inside was a montage of David Bailey's photos. The most amazing keepsake for our superstar boy and it felt like it merged our two journeys; the one at hospital and now this one at home.

Getting home was all I had longed for, and it truly felt blissful having all my little family together. It was all I had dreamed of. Yet some of those concerns and overwhelm I had felt during our last few days at GOSH were proving to be accurate.

Once you're home, people think all is okay. We were all okay, aside from the incurable condition Bailey still had to live with, and myself overcoming the trauma of all that happened since his arrival.

After months of yearning to be home to be a mother to my three boys, now here I was, all my dreams come true, but each day felt heavy – I still woke up with a cloud hanging over my head. Those first moments when you're coming round, and your thoughts slowly re-enter your reality and you realise, 'yes, it is still true.'

I would have moments of sheer bliss – moments where it was all so idyllic with all my boys that I would feel like I had won the life lottery. Then I'd remember cystic fibrosis and how it came crashing into our lives never to leave, and it would infiltrate that moment with just as much venom. I would foresee a torrid future, and my feelings of elation that were making my eyes well, would morph into sentiments of fear and sadness that made my tears overflow and roll down my cheeks. Briskly, I'd wipe them away and carry on as though nothing had happened, like most busy mummas.

Every morning began by getting the bigger two boys ready for school, during which time I would breastfeed Bailey, give him all his meds and do his physio, which entailed fifteen minutes of bouncing on a ball with a PEP mask.

I used to walk with a spring in my step, but instead I now trudged to school. I felt tired, wrecked, damaged, emotional and was still crippled with paranoia about what everybody thought.

I truly believed people were judging me for being so irresponsible to not know my genetic coding – to not know that we carried the CF genes. I kept my head down and made minimal eye contact with anyone. It was probably also a protective sense as well, not wanting people to ask or say too much for fear of breaking down.

I peeled myself off the floor every single day. I found a way to surmount my grief daily to be a mum to three children. I waded my way through emotions throughout the day, swaying between grief, guilt, love, hope, despair, guilt, frustration, disbelief, doubt and a bit more guilt.

My days were spent alone with Bailey, while Harry and Mylo were at school and Kev at work. It was wonderful to have some one-to-one time with him, without nurses and doctors infiltrating our bond, but it also meant I was solely in charge of his wellbeing, which felt overwhelming for some time.

I questioned everything I did for him, even though I was an experienced mother. I contacted the CF team on numerous occasions, with such random queries, such as if he needed Creon when I gave him Calpol, or if he could sit in the waiting area at the GP for his immunisation jabs.

I doubted everything I did for Bailey, because I hadn't been a mum to a child living with cystic fibrosis before.

Bailey's sleep was horrendous. None of my boys slept through until about ten months due to being breastfed. To me, I just accepted that's the life of a mum with a newborn. However, my sleep deprivation with Bailey was like nothing I had ever experienced.

Due to the malabsorption, babies with CF can struggle to go through long stretches without feeding again. I was up and down all night, every night. Some would say it was habit, some would say it was CF-related. I believe that it was a bit of both.

I had to deprive my baby of milk the entire time we were at GOSH. Now finally at home, I was able to feed him on demand as he so wished. At first this was a joyous moment, allowed to be the normal mother I had always craved, but of course it didn't always serve long term. I just couldn't find it within me to keep milk from him after all his deprivation while at hospital.

Kev and I decided to give Bailey a bottle of formula for the 10pm feed in the hope this might help him go longer and allow for a few extra hours sleep. Unfortunately, this landed us in an even worse situation.

Some children with CF can struggle with wind, and this appeared to be true of Bailey. The few nights he had a bottle, he screamed so hard with discomfort that the neighbours could hear. One night it was so bad that I actually resorted to driving to our local A&E as I truly believed he had more stomach and bowel issues.

As soon as I pulled up in the car at 3am, I felt sick. I sat in the hospital carpark wondering if I should go in, knowing if I entered those doors I would once again lose control of my little boy and possibly end up right back at square one; in hospital with my family separated.

Ironically, as I sat there contemplating what might be, Bailey seemed to find comfort in the upright position of his car seat and dozed off to sleep silently. I drove home thankful I didn't need to re-enter the medical world, and carried him carefully in the car seat and set it down on the kitchen floor.

They say you shouldn't let babies sleep in car seats over night, but given it was now almost 4am and the boys would be awake in a couple of hours, I sat on the arm chair in the kitchen and watched him sleep, too scared to even try to attempt putting him back in the cot.

Needless to say, my eyes were soon too heavy to keep open, and after a little doze I woke to Harry and Mylo staring at me most confused as I sat in the kitchen in my coat and woolly hat and Bailey still sleeping in his car seat.

It's no wonder I found it so challenging; dealing with a normal day on a lack of sleep is difficult, so to have such a constant loss of sleep while dealing with so many emotions and traumas, truly was my biggest challenge.

Through no one's fault, everyone believed all was okay now because we were home and Bailey was doing well. Perhaps this is the impression I strived to give once I stepped outside, but each day was tough and heavy, and I know that my boys weren't getting the best version of me as their mummy, which they so deserved.

I was broken, hurting and exhausted.

I washed my hands to the point at which they bled. I washed them constantly, because I was petrified I would pass something to Bailey.

I cleaned the house like an obsessed woman. This was my one point of control, aiming to keep it clean of any potential harmful bacteria that could give Bailey an infection.

Every four weeks I took Bailey to attend his CF clinics with the cystic fibrosis team at GOSH, whose care he would now stay under until he turned eighteen years old.

On our first clinic trip, I had to get the boys to school, before driving to the station to get the train into London. It's fair to say, it didn't go so well.

I managed to get Bailey's bright pink, sticky Fluclox antibiotic on my top, I squirted his sodium chloride in my eye (which really stings, by the way) and then as I was rounding up the troops to get out of the door, Bailey was sick all over Harry's shoes, as well as my own.

But I did it! I made the train in time and felt like a hero. Just a hero with a pink-stained top, one reddened, stinging eye and sick in her shoes.

I actually made it with enough time to get a cup of tea and pop to the ladies' toilets to rinse out the pink stain, but then had a dark, wet spot on my top which instead made it look like a milky leaky boob stain. Brilliant. Winning the day, Laura.

During the clinics, we meet with the consultant, CF nurse, physio and dietician. We wait in our own room to avoid potential contact with other people also there for the CF clinic, and the specialists come to us. They do the usual weight and height, go through his Creon, diet, medicines and physiotherapy.

They also take a cough swab, tickling the back of the throat to make the child cough and use this swab to see if any bacteria grow. If so, they can then determine what antibiotic to prescribe to treat the infection and avoid potential long-term damage.

One week after clinic, my phone rang. I recognised the number as GOSH. As my phone vibrated on the kitchen worktop, a sick feeling developed in my stomach as I knew this was about Bailey's swab results.

I answered and it was Claire from the CF team, and I could tell she was treading carefully with me. I think everyone treaded carefully with me for quite some time as they knew what we had all been through and how fragile and sensitive I was to it all still.

Claire explained that Bailey had grown a common CF-related infection called Pseudomonas. She gently explained that he would need a nebuliser as well as some antibiotic to try to get rid of it, but that sometimes it wasn't possible to get rid of it, and then we would find a way to manage it throughout Bailey's life.

Once the call ended, a rage hit me and I threw my phone, smashing it on the tiled floor. I'm not proud of my actions, but I felt as if I was on my knees trying to stand up, and I kept being pushed back down. Everything that came our way, I tried to stand strong, or even just stay standing, but it was relentless. No matter how hard I tried to care for this child, I just couldn't keep him well.

I left my shattered phone on the floor, and used my negative emotions to clean the house like never before. Bailey was asleep and the boys didn't need picking up for two hours, so I got to work. I steam cleaned the floors, put every single tea towel on a hot wash, I sterilised the sink, I threw away our toothbrush holder and scrubbed the bathroom until my hands were red.

All these things are places where damp stagnant bacteria can fester, which could be where Bailey picked up the germs. That said, he could have picked it up from anywhere, but I hadn't been taking him out too much as I consciously decided I wanted to let his immune system rebuild since being out of GOSH. I think that's why I felt like it was most likely the house that had been the cause, hence my frenzied clean.

The day-to-day reality of this infection meant an extra physio session every evening, and a nebuliser twice a day, which then needed cleaning and sterilising each time. We did this religiously for three months; two physio sessions, two nebuliser sessions and all his usual meds.

The thing with CF is that there is nobody there checking up on you. It's very much down to the parents to make your child's health your total priority. Of course, for the majority of people this is absolutely the case in all children, whether they have CF or not. However, there was a huge sense of responsibility to get it just right and to be totally committed to the medical needs of your child every single day.

I was also acutely aware that all the CF treatments only slow down the process; they rarely stop them. Liver and lung transplants could still eventually be required. It's not about curing CF, it's about managing it and giving those living with CF more time. Treatments are simply extending the time everything takes to worsen, in turn extending life expectancy. The outcome will be the same, it will just be a lot slower.

You sometimes get to a point where you feel like you are beating CF – you're getting on with life and manging the condition well with meds and physio. Then it comes along and hits you in the face and shakes you by the shoulders vigorously, just to remind you it's still here and who is actually in control. An infection is this rigorous shake.

After three months of nebuliser, we managed to clear the Pseudomonas, which was a huge achievement and relief to all. Shortly after Bailey grew another bug, which again Claire called to inform me of, with her usual tentative tone.

Every time Bailey caught an infection, my first fears were if he had to go in for IV antibiotics, and we wound find ourselves back at GOSH, all separated once again.

This time Bailey didn't require the nebuliser, but although they were going to try antibiotics from home, if that didn't work he might need to be admitted.

I still always asked Claire so many questions, and always seemed to be one step ahead – jumping into the future to see what might be, rather than accepting what she was telling me about the here and now. Love me or loathe me, she couldn't deny I adored my little baby boy.

I feel like I'm going to spend the rest of my life asking questions that nobody can answer. I like to be presented with the facts, and for there to be definites. There aren't any with CF; it's vague, each case is different and there's no known set path.

One definite I wanted to check was that Harry and Mylo did not have cystic fibrosis. Although the CF team felt confident neither boy had CF, they couldn't guarantee it without a sweat test, so I decided to find out for absolute certainty.

People with cystic fibrosis lose a lot of salt, so one way to diagnose it is with a sweat test. I took all three boys into London, where Harry and Mylo had an appointment at GOSH to have a sweat test. Both boys had a little watch-like device strapped to their wrist. A small electrical stimulation is applied to encourage the sweat glands to release sweat. The sweat is collected and then tested. People with CF have more chloride in their sweat, but thankfully both boys' results came back negative for cystic fibrosis. Only time would tell if they were genetic carriers like Kev and I, or if they had escaped the CF gene altogether.

Kev and I now knew we carried the gene, and Harry and Mylo would have a blood test to find out aged eighteen. My sister Jules and Kev's sister Clair were tested, and in fact they both carry the gene, meaning all their children will also need to find out if they are CF gene carriers when they became adults and perhaps want their own children.

The ripple effect of this whole thing reached far beyond my family of five. While I felt a huge sense of guilt that I had brought this family heritage to the surface, I also felt that if it wasn't for Bailey's diagnosis, we wouldn't all be so informed.

Kev and I never had the information we all now had. The next generation could now make informed decisions when they met their loved ones and wanted to have a family. I'm not saying what anyone should do with such information as that's personal, but what I am saying is that Kev and I went in blind.

We were both blindsided by the fact Bailey was diagnosed with CF. We didn't see it coming, and not in a million years if someone had asked would I have even thought about CF. However, this is the case for many people who have a child with cystic fibrosis, as so few people know they carry the faulty gene.

Yet here we were, with all four newly-informed genetic carriers, with a total of seven children who will now request a genetic test when they are adults, all because we decided to have a third child, Bailey. Because of him, we now had the knowledge we'd never had before, but at what cost to Bailey? I couldn't shake this image of him being our family scapegoat.

All this time, I still struggled to accept Bailey's CF diagnosis. I kept telling myself they'd got it wrong; that they'd got the blood results mixed up and diagnosed the wrong baby. He was so well and beautifully perfect, that I couldn't grasp the concept that there was anything wrong with him at all.

One day I was on my way out to meet friends for a coffee and I kissed Bailey as I picked him up to carry him to the car. I then coincidentally licked my lips and the salty taste hit me. People with CF have saltier skin due to higher salt losses. This kiss confirmed it for me far beyond any medical test could. My son had cystic fibrosis and I had to find a way to accept that.

I was hurting. It's as simple as that. I felt buried under all the hurt, guilt and overthinking, and I couldn't seem to find my way out.

Meanwhile, true to form, Kev was his usual positive, hopeful self. He willingly researched online, followed CF inspirations on social media and remained solid in his faith that Bailey was going to be not just OK, but great. He believed in the rumours of miracle drugs about to launch soon, knowing that CF in Bailey's lifetime would be very different to times gone by.

I wanted to be where he was, and I admired how quickly he had managed to get himself there. I was a weight that was trailing far behind, laden down by my pain and guilt.

I was conscious not to use Kev as my crutch as I wanted to stand strong and independent as I had done before. Although I admit to crying into his chest on several occasions, and he catching me just as I was about to crumple, I had a will to find my way towards renewed strength.

My turning point was actually after suffering my first and only panic attack one night in December. I honestly thought I was having a stroke, but after Kev called 111 and the ambulance crew were at my bedside, they managed to calm my breathing.

This was a moment of realisation that I had to sort myself out. I had to get help and I had to start taking care of me, so I could take care of my family.

That night was proof to me just what stress I had been under for over half a year now. Fatigue, traumas, life changes, life-long conditions, emotions and all on top of being a generally busy mummy to three little ones.

I see this panic attack as everything coming to a head and finally finding a way out. I'd spent months trying to prove I was okay and keeping myself measured, in control and on show. I had taken hit after hit, and like a baby learning to walk, I kept falling but getting back up.

As long as I kept standing up again, I grew stronger. As I learnt more, I accepted more of what was, what is and what will be. I realised that I could never allow it all to pile up like that again, and so I found a way to manage better.

Out of falls, come utter strength, and out of parenting comes unconditional love.

I finally acknowledged I had to find a way to deal with what had happened, and what lay before us, which is when I turned to a couple of friends, Karen and Lisa, for their support. Between both their professional coaching expertise, they steered me to find a way to see Bailey as Bailey, rather than CF.

I feared people would only see Bailey as cystic fibrosis, and that's all he would be known for, but maybe I felt that because that's all I was so focused on. I wasn't seeing his beautiful smile, his love of balls or his sweet giggle. CF is just one part of his make up; just one factor that makes Bailey, Bailey. My son has blue eyes, blonde hair, a cheeky face, cystic fibrosis, two big brothers, pale skin and loves balls. There, just like that. It slots within everything else that makes my boy himself.

I used to look at photos of myself before Bailey's arrival, and I envied the ignorant, naïve girl looking back at me. I used to stare at pictures of myself pregnant, wondering what was going on in my womb at that time, if his meconium was already building up then and just how I had no idea what awaited me.

Every time I stared into a more recent photo of myself, there was so much sadness in my eyes. I had so much to be thankful for, but there was something behind my eyes, like a darkness that I had no control over.

I learned tools to help me cope. I had unknowingly used running as a coping strategy while in GOSH, which was something I continued at home. As a result, I signed up to run the London Marathon for the CF Trust, which was later cancelled due to the COVID-19 pandemic, so I ran it virtually. I ran the twenty-six miles around my village, with friends and family there to cheer me on and a few friends who ran most of the distance with me.

It was such a humbling experience and in hindsight I'm glad the London event was cancelled to allow me to complete the race with loved ones around me – those who helped me so much at my time of need.

This perhaps gave the illusion I was strong and had conquered this whole thing, when in fact it was my desperate attempt to feel like I was doing something, anything, to help my son and repair the damage I believed I had caused our little boy.

I lived in fear of Bailey being admitted, so-much-so that I also had to learn coping techniques for this too, writing down a plan so I knew what to do when it hit us. Although, three years later, I do admit to still not having wiped off the 'Welcome home baby Bailey' message Kev wrote on the blackboard in the kitchen, as superstition gets the better of me.

Whatever was suggested, I took it on board and worked on it. I wanted to heal and cope and move forward, but I was still not myself. I longed to be myself again, but that person was never seen again. Instead, I became someone new, and once I acknowledged that and stepped into my new self, I was free to move forwards.

The traumatic event of being at GOSH and the CF diagnosis has changed me forever. I can't go back to being the person I was, because she doesn't exist anymore. She had two sons and no idea what cystic fibrosis was. The new me has three sons and has become a novice expert in the CF world.

I used to think I was irreparably damaged, but I now believe I am irrevocably changed. I used to let my story hold me back, but now I own our story, accept it and use it to offer support and inspiration to others.

Thankfully, as Bailey began to grow and flourish, so did I. I grew in strength and I learned to accept the cystic fibrosis. As murmurings of new drugs became louder, I too started to buy into the idea that something was on the cusp of changing the cystic fibrosis world forever.

Visit www.laura-barrett.co.uk to view a gallery of photos of Bailey's journey from Great Ormond Street Hospital to today.

HOPE

As I write this book, I'm the proud mother of three boys; Harry, aged nine, Mylo, aged seven, and Bailey, aged three. The youngest of the three has the cheekiest character, crazy long, tatty blonde hair, striking blue eyes, a round belly, is part of a tight brotherhood trio and expresses a zest for life that many would envy.

I don't see anything else.

Bailey thrives in life. He runs over a mile for a jog, he plays football and rugby with his brothers, he walks for miles in his wellies finding puddles and mud galore (while I hover alongside, antibac hand gel at the ready). He enjoys doing his daily physio and takes his Creon tablets independently.

He does not question.

He has not been readmitted into hospital.

Of course, questions will come. Hospital stays continue to be a possibility. However, never before have I witnessed such a comeback.

From the frail little boy in hospital surrounded by machines and tubes, to the hysterical, cheeky ringleader that starts chants at our family dinner table.

This is hope. This is inspiration. This is what you need to hold onto from this story.

I would never have believed that the little baby I witnessed could become this child. I know you can never imagine how your baby will be a few years down the line; what will they look like? How will they sound? Yet when your baby has had a tough start in life, that's even more impossible to imagine.

Of course, I am acutely aware that everyone's CF journey will be different and that some people don't get to bring their babies home from hospital at all for other reasons, so I totally appreciate how fortunate we truly are.

Equally, we know that Bailey is just a short way into living his life with cystic fibrosis. We have no idea what awaits our dear child, but right now this boy can. This boy does. This boy will.

Bailey is the little piece of the puzzle that completed our family in a way we could never have foreseen. His sassy nature is devilishly cute, while he lives life in a way that makes you want to make the most of every moment in every day. Whatever pain was experienced; the joy he has brought us all already in his short little life far outweighs any heartache.

To quote Bailey's big brother, "A cystic fibrosis Bailey is better than no Bailey."

Bailey is no different from his brothers. We've never made him an exception and his brothers have never treated him differently from their other sibling. They are a triple pack and their genetic makeup has no bearing. That said, Harry and Mylo are exemplary. They ask questions so they're informed, remind us to give the Creon and steer Bailey away from stagnant water should he get too close. Their protection for him adds to their brotherly bond – along with their regular rough and tumbles.

We've had to be ready to receive and respond to a myriad of questions, often landing on our laps at the untimeliest of situations. Calmly we gather our thoughts, and explain it clearly, concisely and truthfully. I will not lie to them, nor Bailey. We owe Bailey that. It is his body, his condition and something he lives with.

Every time we receive some news that isn't great, I restock our Dettol stores, clean the house and go for a run. They have become my go-to reactions with any changes and news on Bailey's health. And that evening, I allow myself time to adjust to the new situation and wrap my head around what's being presented to us, then I get up the next morning and keep going.

Despite very different approaches and ways of coping in the early days, it amazes me how aligned Kev and I are today. I'm now able to read and research CF alongside my husband, and we both feel fury bound to ensure anyone in our families who could carry the CF gene are aware of the fact. We never want anyone we know to live and endure what we did, nor be impacted by this condition, so we speak openly about CF and do what we can to raise awareness of it.

The past three years for us as a couple were undoubtedly the most challenging of our time together. Not testing to our love or relationship, but a time that's required space mixed with closeness, understanding with questioning, support yet independence, respect for each other's own thoughts while suggesting new ideas at the right time.

Without any shadow of a doubt it's required more love, respect and communication than anything we've ever known. There is nobody I would rather be on this journey with, and while we have found a common ground, our opposite ways have sat in beautiful harmony, lifting one side when the other dipped, and showing me how if he can get to a point of frustrated acceptance, then so can (and must) I. We've grown as people in strength, understanding, empathy and love, while talking about things that I wish never had to be discussed, but communicating in such a mature, respectful way.

When you can come out of this with so much love and support, you know you've found your partner for life.

We are also in this CF world for life. However, whatever awaits our family, we will be at the helm steering this ship together and guiding our boys to a life of their wildest dreams, ready to face any adversity CF throws at us.

I hope Kev's love of exercise is so deeply implanted in all our boys that they never stop their weekend jogs, nor lose their love of rugby and football.

I pray the positive mindsets we are programming them with will serve Bailey through tough times and lead them all on to believe they can achieve whatever they desire, CF or not.

Bailey wants to be a rugby player, like his daddy.

Rugby top, scrum hat and kit bag at the ready by the front door, hours of purposeful practice and an unfaltering belief; watch this space.

At the time of writing this, longed-for hope was offered to the CF community.

The 'miracle' drug Kaftrio (also known as Trikafta in America) was approved by the NHS in England on 30th June 2020, allowing anyone over the age of twelve with one or two Delta F508 CF gene, access to a new way of living with CF.

Reports coming in from America of those people using the treatment were days of purges hacking up mucus previously stuck in their lungs, improved lung function and less infections – overall this lead to improved health, wellbeing and lifestyle, not to mention life expectancy.

In January 2022 the eligible age for Kaftrio in the UK was reduced to six years old, helping a further 1,500 children between the age of six and twelve who have the correct genotype.

Prior to this there was Orkambi, suitable only for those with double Delta F508 CF genes from age two years old. This catered for just under half of the CF community.

Kaftrio could treat around ninety percent of the CF population, including Bailey.

Maybe we've just reached the point in time when CF is no longer a life sentence? A condition that plants an age above your head that you simply try to either live up to, or outlive.

Maybe one day CF will be as treatable as HIV is today, which back in the eighties was terminal? It might mean that new parents aren't left bereft when they hear the cystic fibrosis diagnosis, but are offered so much hope with a tinge of nonchalance because it's so easily treated?

A new cystic fibrosis generation now exists – the ones who have the hope their predecessors never did. The children who will be the evidence of just what Kaftrio can do for a life with CF and just how old, in our wildest dreams, they can live life.

Even so, a cure is still yet to be found, and for around ten percent of the CF population Kaftrio cannot help them.

To anyone touched by cystic fibrosis, we will fight until the letters CF stand for Cure Found.

Visit www.laura-barrett.co.uk to view a gallery of photos of Bailey's journey from Great Ormond Street Hospital to today.

SUPPORT GUIDES

When your child receives a medical diagnosis or is admitted to hospital, your world can fall apart in the most inexplicable way. Often, words simply aren't sufficient to articulate your pain, so the only person who really understands is someone watching on with empathy, who has lived your heartache for themselves.

I am that person, reaching out to you from these pages, offering my deepest and most sincere care and compassion. Consider each piece of advice a hug from me to you, a whisper telling you to 'get up, go again, you can do this', and a nod of complete and utter knowing.

Every suggestion in these support guides is here to help you find your way with a little more knowledge and comfort, and equip you with tools and tips that I hope prove valuable at this time – the very ones I learnt and used.

The advice won't heal, it won't change your circumstances and it won't take you back, but my hope is that it will give you some information you perhaps crave or don't want to ask out loud, allow you to acknowledge that all your feelings and concerns are justified, and provide you with tools to help you cope, forgive and enable you to move forwards.

While our journey was with a cystic fibrosis diagnosis, the following information is relevant whether your baby is having a trying start to life in hospital, or your little one has been diagnosed with a condition of any sort. I pray that you can find something here to help you process this news, manage the journey you're on and step forwards with strength and courage towards the future that awaits your family.

I've collaborated with specialists in their field to provide accurate and helpful information, and who better than the very people that touched our lives throughout our journey, including my Cognitive Behavioural Therapist and my breastfeeding and expressing specialist. Plus, fellow Great Ormond Street Hospital friend, Liana – not a specialist, but a hugely qualified mummy of five.

This isn't a one-size-fits-all rule book. There's no definitive way to cope in these situations, and everyone will find different ways to get through, so please take what you find helpful and leave on the page what you don't want. Many lifestyle elements can be implemented, ignored or simply approached differently.

Challenging times test us to our limits, and my hope is that with these support guides you will not only survive the now, but thrive when you come out the other side and begin to piece back together life, and your dear self.

Chapters

1. Coping mechanisms; finding yours
2. Guilt; accepting it and healing from it
3. Journaling; the why and how
4. Hospital stays; advice for parents and visiting guests
5. Expressing to breastfeeding; support at times of distress
6. Cleaning; for all children who require clean environments
7. Cystic fibrosis facts and questions, answered

CHAPTER 1
Coping mechanisms; finding yours
Written in collaboration with Lisa du Plessis, BABCP Accredited Cognitive Behavioural Psychotherapist

While staying at Great Ormond Street, there was a tipping point where I literally thought to myself, 'If we have to stay here for the foreseeable, then I am staying here on my terms, in my way.'

For me this meant collecting my laptop and running gear on one of my homeward trips so I could both work and run, taking in my bag of protein and shaker for breakfast, bringing in my own box of peppermint tea bags for my nightly tipple and ordering my own thermos bottle to use rather than the plastic cups from the kitchen. And of course, journaling Bailey's journey.

As you can see, these things ranged in significance, but they all made me feel a little bit more 'normal'.

I didn't realise it at the time, but they were my coping strategies, something I only later learnt while having Cognitive Behavioural Therapy (CBT) sessions with my friend Lisa du Plessis.

Everyone's coping strategies will be different, and it's important to find yours. They can be something to help you feel slightly more in control, help ease the stress or simply find some peace in the chaos. Something to help you adjust to the event while maintaining your mental and emotional wellbeing.

You might find a need for coping strategies for a number of situations, both while in hospital, once home or simply to get your head around a diagnosis – finding a way to accept it.

Once I got home, I continued to run and work as I had done while at GOSH, but I also had to use other tools too.

I found that cleaning was a huge coping strategy. I cleaned that house until it sparkled in a bid to keep it free from any potential bacteria that might be harmful to Bailey and cause an infection (see chapter 6 for more information on cleaning).

I had to clean. It was like a compulsion. Not obsessive, but a means to be in control and feel like I was doing something to help in Bailey's plight.

I also found that Bailey's monthly CF clinics really took their toll. I would feel anxious a few days prior and build it up in my head, then when I got home from the clinic I would feel exhausted, emotionally drained and didn't want to do anything, be it cook dinner, housework or work.

In order to handle these better, I wrote down my questions I wanted to ask in advance of the clinic, and I always made sure I had dinner sorted for that evening, that I was on top of all my work and admin and would then allow myself to relax on those evenings with a hot bath, my journal and wallow in my own self-pity. In doing this my world could momentarily grind to a halt while I re-configured, and by the morning I would feel strong again and ready to take on the world once more.

While having CBT with Lisa, I learnt more useful coping tools, which helped me further along my healing and acceptance process.

One key coping tool was to plan for the eventuality that scared me the most. I feared Bailey would be readmitted for IV antibiotics, which would mean we were back to living separately after our family had already been apart for so long. I had to face this situation head on and devise a plan for my family and I to cope should this become a reality.

I drew up the plan, outlining childcare solutions, when the boys could visit, what I would pack in my bag and something nice to celebrate Bailey's homecoming at the end, which was a special meal at our favourite restaurant. By doing this, it instantly showed me that I would be able to manage and I had all the solutions when I applied myself – the fear was worse than the reality, as is often the case.

I also couldn't bring myself to read any research online or follow any CF-related social media channels. I didn't want it in my day-to-day scroll as it gave me a sick feeling in the pit of my stomach every time. I learnt that in fact this is exactly what I needed to do to help normalise it, and also dis-associate Bailey's journey with anything else I was reading. When I let it in, I found that it offered a supportive community and hope, through CF inspirations such as Ben Mudge and Marc Cotterill, for example.

Being unable to talk about certain events that took place was also holding back my healing process. I couldn't bring myself to even say the very words themselves; cystic fibrosis. Nor could I relay the moment of handing Bailey over at GOSH without breaking down. There were certain 'blocking' points that I needed to clear and in order to do this I had to write it down and read it, repeatedly. Again, this helps normalise the event in your mind.

Working with Lisa helped me immeasurably to get my head around both the trauma of all that happened, and also learn to live with Bailey's diagnosis and all that the future entails. It felt only right, therefore, that I should share some of her awesomeness with you in the hope she too can help you cope. What I love about CBT is that it's learning some key principles and tools that can help you in all areas of life, from stressful times to simple parenting. Cue, Lisa du Plessis ...

What are coping mechanisms?

Coping mechanisms and coping strategies are the behaviours, thoughts, and emotions that we use to adjust to the changes that occur in our lives. There are many coping mechanisms people use, some of which can be positive (effective) and others negative (ineffective).

Ineffective coping mechanisms (also referred to as maladaptive coping), are often applied during stressful events and usually unconsciously, meaning we don't even realise. They may appear to help us in the short term, but in the longer term they accidentally make our problems worse, which can impact negatively on our emotional and mental wellbeing.

Effective coping mechanisms (also known as adaptive coping) help improve mental and emotional wellbeing. People who are able to adjust to stressful or traumatic situations through productive coping mechanisms may be less likely to experience anxiety, depression and other mental health problems, longer term.

Coping with anxiety or stress can be identified as being either active or avoidant. Active coping strategies involve an awareness of the stressful event/issue, followed by attempts to reduce the negative outcome. In contrast, avoidant coping is characterised by ignoring the issue, often resulting in activities that aid in the denial of the problem, such as drinking, sleeping, isolating, avoiding people and the subject.

We may or may not have an awareness of how we cope, until we really make an effort to understand our responses to stress or anxiety. Here are examples of some of the ways we may already cope with stressful life events:

- **Humour.** Pointing out the funny aspects of the problem is thought to help deal with small failures.
- **Seeking support.** Asking for help, or finding emotional support from family members or friends can be an effective way of maintaining emotional health during a stressful period.

- **Problem solving.** This aims to locate the source of the problem and determine solutions.
- **Relaxation.** Engaging in relaxing activities or practicing calming techniques can help manage stress and improve overall coping.
- **Exercise.** Regular exercise, such as running or team sports, is a good way to handle the stress of a situation.
- **Adjusting expectations.** Anticipating various outcomes to scenarios in life may assist in preparing for the stress associated with any given change or event.
- **Denial.** Avoidance of the issue altogether may lead to denying that a problem even exists.
- **Self-blame.** Internalising the issue and blaming oneself (beyond just taking responsibility for one's actions) can lead to low self-esteem and sometimes depression.
- **Venting.** In moderation, expressing emotions can be healthy, but ruminating on the negative can lead to strained relationships over time.
- **Unhealthy self-soothing or numbing.** These are unhelpful behaviours that may feel soothing in the short term, but may turn into an unhealthy addiction if it becomes a habit. Examples include excessive working, drinking alcohol, taking substances, excessive use of video games, binge-eating or restricting dietary intake and excessive exercising.
- **Avoidance.** Actively trying to avoid reminders, memories, media and people that are relevant to the stressor may reduce stress in the very short term, but just delays the ability to resolve the problems related to the issue and can increase stress.
- **Escape.** Some people may withdraw from friends and become socially isolated. They may absorb themselves in a solitary activity, such as watching TV, reading or spending time online.
- **Compulsions and risk-taking.** Stress can cause some people to seek an adrenaline rush through compulsive or risk-taking behaviours such as gambling, unsafe sex, experimenting with drugs, theft or reckless driving.
- **Self-harm.** People may engage in self-harming behaviours to cope with extreme stress or trauma.

Thoughts, emotions and behaviours

Cognitive Behavioural Therapy (CBT) sounds complicated, but it's just a type of talking therapy that focuses on your thoughts (cognitions), how you act or react (behaviour) and the relationship of both with your feelings (emotions).

CBT is the most scientific and evidence-based psychological treatment for many mental health problems, such as anxiety disorders, trauma and depression, but it's also really effective in everyday life. For example, managing stress, feeling happier, coping with change, improving relationships, accepting difficult experiences or past events and increasing self-confidence.

In any given event or situation, you will have a series of thoughts (these may be positive, negative or neutral), and these thoughts will impact your emotions and then possibly dictate your behaviour.

This is why we look at the relationship with our thinking, emotions and behaviour in CBT. When we understand that relationship in ourselves, we can reduce our stress levels and improve our ability to cope with stressful events.

The order of the relationship between emotions, behaviour and thoughts can change too. For example, changing your behaviour can influence your thoughts and emotions, such as going for a walk or working out.

You can incorporate CBT into your everyday life simply by understanding your thinking and behavioural patterns, and making small changes that help you feel happier, healthier, more productive and relaxed. It's learning about yourself, trying new strategies and creating new habits.

A range of Cognitive Behavioural coping strategies are listed below, but what's imperative is finding the ones that work well for you and prove effective in your life. There's no right nor wrong – just knowing which coping tools or mechanisms work for you is what's important here and you will only find this out if you practise them a few times.

Self-Monitoring

This is at the core of all cognitive behavioural coping strategies. In order to address a problem or symptom, we need to first become aware of it through self-monitoring. There are a number of steps to self-monitoring, which can be easily learned and quickly applied to your life. Simply keeping a diary of your mood with a daily mood rating, is one example.[2]

Setting and Managing Goals

Goals and things that you want to accomplish in the future can give your life purpose and direction, as well as motivate healthy behaviours focused on improving your life. Don't make your goals too big though, otherwise they can become overwhelming and a source of stress. Just making a realistic plan or list for the week or day ahead can help you reduce stress. When you do have a goal in mind, it is vital to break the goal down into smaller, achievable steps.

Cognitive Restructuring

How we evaluate and think about ourselves, other people and events can have a major impact on our mood. Sometimes we need to change the way we think to reframe unhelpful or negative thoughts or evaluations, and modify them to help improve your mood and make better choices with regard to behaviours.[3]

If a friend ignores you when you see her out shopping, you could worry that you've upset her, you could think she is rude, or you could simply assume she is in a rush and not let it affect you. What you think in this situation will determine how you respond and behave after the event.

Behavioural Activation

When people feel depressed or anxious, they may be less likely to do the things they enjoy. Behavioural activation helps people get more active in areas of their life that are pleasurable and enjoyable. Being more connected and involved with these experiences can improve your mood, and can also be a positive distraction.

---

[2] Download this free Mood Diary worksheet https://www.getselfhelp.co.uk/media/if4gnuow/mooddiary.pdf.
[3] Download this free Thought Record Sheet to help reframe some of your negative thoughts https://www.getselfhelp.co.uk/media/1cafl2ue/thoughtrecordsheet7.pdf.

Progressive Muscle Relaxation

Using cognitive-behavioural relaxation exercises can be an effective way to reduce your stress and anxiety. Progressive Muscle Relaxation (PMR) focuses on a person alternating between tensing and relaxing different muscle groups throughout the body, often starting at the feet and working up to your face.

Breathing Exercises

Breathing is very important when managing stress. When we have a stress response in our body, our breathing automatically increases. Why? It's the survival mechanism switching on, called 'fight or flight'.

Once the danger sensor (the amygdala in our brains) triggers off a message for potential danger, adrenalin is released into the body to prepare us to stay and fight, or run away from that danger. When we get this response due to stress rather than actual physical danger, we need a way to calm the body down again. Physical exercise and breathing exercises are the fastest methods to control this reaction.

Breathing automatically increases when we are anxious or stressed, because our body thinks we need to fight or run, so it wants to send more oxygen to your muscles to energise them. When you don't fight or run, you can start to feel breathless for no reason and this can feel scary. We then often try to control our breathing by taking deep breaths, but these frequently lead to accidentally hyperventilating, which could lead to a panic attack.

Following a breathing exercise stabilises your blood gases (oxygen and carbon dioxide), often stopping a panic attack rapidly. Plus, it sends a message to your brain to turn off the fight or flight response and begin to reverse the process. Try the breathing exercise below:

- Take a normal-sized breath and hold it for 15 seconds. Breathe out slowly.
- Next breath, hold for 10 seconds, and breathe out.
- Next breath, hold for 5 seconds, and breathe out.
- Repeat 4 more times, so 5 rounds in total.

Exercise

Many of us may already know that exercise is excellent for reducing the physical effects of stress. It uses up excess energy in the body released through the fight/flight response. Once we are physically calmer, our thinking is more rational, leading to an overall reduction in stress.

Cardiovascular exercise, such as running, works the most effectively, however walking and strength exercise are also useful if you're less mobile, injured or in an environment where exercise is not possible. For example, when working with adults and teenagers who experience anxiety or stress at work or school, I advise doing 30-50 squats in a toilet cubicle to use up nervous energy.

Exercise also releases endorphins and serotonin. These natural chemicals in our body help us reduce pain, sleep better and improve our mood in the most natural way.

Routine

Humans are creatures of habit, and although we may love moments of spontaneity and surprise, we feel at our most comfortable when we know what is about to happen and we can follow a plan or routine.

Schedules and routines are important because they create a structure, give us a sense of accomplishment, and let us and others know how we are managing.

However, be realistic about your plan and don't cram in too much, otherwise it will add to your stress, not ease it. A simple routine to organise your day may include:

- Wake up at the same time every day.
- Bath/shower as if you were going out.
- Get dressed and manage self-care.
- Stay on top of housework and laundry if possible.
- Eat three meals a day at regular times with snacks in between.
- Plan a daily schedule of self-care such as exercise, meditation or relaxation.
- Reduce your use of devices and social media.

Problem-Solving

There is a difference between problems that can be solved and hypothetical worry.

Worrying is actually a negative thought process. When we fall into a pattern of worrying, we often have future-based thoughts involving worst case scenarios and all the possible problems that may happen in the future. They usually go round and round in our heads. Often, we are so anxious that we can't think clearly, so we never allow our minds to find any real solutions. Instead, we often just dwell on our worst fears.

Problem-solving is different – it is a constructive thought process. It helps us focus on how we can flexibly and effectively deal with the problem head on. Problem-solving involves understanding the problem and thinking of the best possible solutions, examining the costs and benefits for each. Depending on what we've highlighted in the costs and benefits, we then devise an action plan and follow it through, then step back and evaluate how well we have dealt with the problem.

Before we can start to problem solve though, we need to understand whether our concern is a solvable problem. To identify a problem, you need to ask yourself is this a real and likely problem I am concerned about? Is the problem something I have control over? Is the problem something that is happening now?

If yes, then you can start the problem-solving process to work on these issues. In CBT we often use a six stage problem-solving plan.

1. Identify or define the problem.
2. Generate possible solutions or options.
3. From the possible list of solutions, identify your preferred options and cross out the ones that you don't believe are relevant.
4. Look at the advantages and disadvantages of the possible solutions, and from this decide on an action plan.
5. Write out your action plan and implement it.
6. Evaluate the outcome. If you are not happy with the outcome, go back to step 2 and repeat.

There are some great online resources providing a worksheet to prompt you.[4]

---

[4] Download this free problem-solving worksheet from
https://www.getselfhelp.co.uk/media/3j3dpzej/problemsolvingworksheet.pdf.

Decision-Making Pros and Cons (Cost Benefit Analysis)

When faced with a decision, we may not know what the best choice is, leaving us paralysed. One way to move forward is to weigh the short and long-term pros and cons of a situation to help identify the best path to take.

Healthy eating and nutrition

Eating healthily and regularly is not only a necessity for our physical wellbeing, but there's scientific evidence to highlight how it affects our mental wellbeing too.[5] From eating regularly to prevent blood sugars from dropping (which for some people can mimic symptoms of anxiety,) to the types of food we eat – what we feed our bodies can really impact our mood.

For example, zinc, which is found in beef, ginger, liver, milk, oysters, sunflower, pumpkin seeds and whole grains, has been proven to help reduce depressive symptoms. A huge psychiatric study evidenced that depressed adults have lower zinc levels than non-depressed adults.[6] The lower the zinc concentration in the blood the more severe the depression was, so-much-so that zinc levels have now become a bio marker for treating resistant depression.

The three other most researched and influential nutrients on mood (specifically depressed mood) are:

- Magnesium – found in almonds, cashews, mineral water, parsnips and wholegrain cereals.
- Vitamin B6 – found in cereal, chicken, fish, egg yolk and legumes.
- Folic acid – found in beans, eggs, green leafy vegetables, lentils, organic meats and yeast.

Hydration

Water improves brain function, yet there is also a growing body of scientific research studying the correlation between hydration and mood disorders, such as anxiety and depression. Even mild dehydration has been

---

5 Janet Polivy and C Peter Herman, Mental Health and Eating Behaviours, *Canadian Journal of Public Health,* July 2005.
6 Petrilli MA, Kranz TM, Kleinhaus K, et al. 'The Emerging Role for Zinc in Depression and Psychosis', *Frontier of Pharmacology.* 2017;8:414. Published June, 2017.

found to have a direct impact on how we feel, making people prone to irritation and lowering mood.

Sleep hygiene

Insomnia has a direct impact on our mood and functioning. Quite simply, when we get regular sleep, we feel happier and more energetic.

Sleep hygiene is a buzz word today with many of us considering our behavioural and environmental setting to promote healthy sleep. However, it was originally developed for use in the treatment of mild to moderate insomnia by behavioural psychologists. During sleep hygiene education, patients learn about healthy sleep habits and are encouraged to follow a set of recommendations to improve their sleep. Research from the Harvard university shows that CBT and consequent sleep hygiene was more effective than sleep medication at treating insomnia.[7] See below for a general sleep hygiene tips.[8]

Positive Affirmations

Positive affirmations are more than just feel good self-talk and positive declarations – they are statements that are repeated to embolden and uplift the person saying them.

Cognitive behavioural research highlighted that a positive affirmation is actually part of the lingo of the brain. Our brains are very straightforward about their dialect rules, so they need to be written in a very specific way, outlined below.

1. **Present tense.** Change any 'I am going to', 'I should do' or 'I will', to 'I am'.
2. **Positive words.** Leave out words such as 'can't', 'don't' or 'won't'.
3. **Statements of real fact and truth.** Omit words such as 'might' or 'could'.

---

[7] *Archives of Internal Medicine*, September 27th 2004 issue.
[8] Find more sleep hygiene tips here https://www.getselfhelp.co.uk/docs/Sleep.pdf.

Visualisation

Visualisation or imagery is a powerful CBT treatment that helps treat trauma, anxiety and depression, and it's also a great confidence building tool. We can use imagery to manage stress by visualising a positive event, memory or predicted scenario. We layer the image with colours, sounds, smells and feelings. For example, get a picture in your mind of a beautiful view you have seen on holiday. Try to add details of colour or scenery.

Next add in the sound and possible smells. How did you feel when you were there? This can trick our brains into feeling as though we may be there and we can feel more relaxed.

This tool is also useful for visualising future-based events, helping you feel more confident when the event takes place as it may feel familiar.

Journaling

Journaling is very popular at the moment and for good reason. Writing down our thoughts and feelings can be cathartic and helps us to process what is going on in our minds. It can also help you monitor your emotions.

It's your private journal, so you can express confidential thoughts, feelings and memories, which can help you rationalise what is happening in your life. (See more on journaling in chapter 3.)

Meditation

Mindfulness meditation within cognitive behavioural therapy builds upon the principles of CBT by teaching us to consciously pay attention to our environment, thoughts and feelings without placing any judgments upon us. We can learn how to use cognitive methods and mindfulness meditation to interrupt the automatic thoughts or behavioural processes that can trigger stress.

Mindfulness meditation helps us learn how to identify our sense of being and see ourselves as separate from our cognitions (thoughts) and feelings. This disconnect can allow us to become liberated from thought patterns in which negative cognitions or behaviours may be replayed over and over. Mindfulness meditation is relaxation for our brain.

Gratitude

Feeling thankful for positive parts of our day may seem cheesy and unrealistic when we feel low, but training our brains to find small positives to be happy and grateful about can really boost our mood and help us cope with stress.

When we are down and stressed, our brains can develop a cognitive bias, which means we look for the bad things that reinforce our feelings of stress and why we feel low. However, we lose sight of the small, important parts of our life that we can take for granted. Creating a new habit of finding five things to be grateful about each day can help focus us on the positives in our lives.

Music

Music is very powerful and can affect our behaviours, thoughts and mood, depending on what we listen to. When we feel sad, we tend to play sad music, but that doesn't help us feel better. Choosing happy, upbeat music can lift our mood and really energise us. Make a happy playlist, full of your favourite uplifting and joyful songs with a cheerful beat.

Art

Adult colouring books and painting by numbers are excellent ways to relax and switch off from worries. Numerous scientific studies highlight the positive link between visual and creative art and a reduction in stress levels.

Talking

This is so important as a stress-busting tool and a way to get support from your loved ones who know you best. Talking any problems through with a good friend or family member can really lighten the load.

Laughing

According to research, laughter therapy is a cognitive-behavioural therapy that could make physical, psychological, and social relationships healthy, ultimately improving the quality of life.[9] Laughter therapy, as a non-pharmacological, alternative treatment, has a positive effect on the mental

---

[9] Yim J, *Therapeutic Benefits of Laughter in Mental Health: A Theoretical Review*, Tohoku J Exp Med. 2016 Jul

health and the immune system. Decreasing stress-making hormones found in the blood, laughter can mitigate the effects of stress, plus laughter therapy does not require specialised preparations.

Screaming into a pillow

Many mental health experts believe that screaming is therapeutic in nature. Once you find the way to completely let out everything you are feeling, your brain automatically relaxes. There's something very satisfying about shouting at the top of your lungs, however it's just not socially acceptable unless you are at a sports stadium or concert. Whatever it is that you're feeling, which has led to an emotional build up, needs to, and probably should be, let out before it turns itself into a real problem. Screaming into a pillow will muffle the sound, but still gives you the emotional release.

Social Media

Research shows that there is an association between social media use and mental health problems, on the basis of a distorted and socially constructed reality.[10] Reduce your time on social media and spend more time in real life to help lift your mood.

---

[10] Keles et al, 'A systematic review: the influence of social media on depression, anxiety and psychological distress in adolescents', *International Journal of Adolescence and Youth*, March 2019.

CHAPTER 2
Guilt; accepting it and healing from it

Guilt. The overriding emotion. I couldn't cope with the guilt. The guilt was paralysing. I felt guilt for Bailey for giving him his cystic fibrosis and for him enduring so much, so young. I felt guilt for Kev for even mentioning having a third child and bringing this crashing into our lives. I felt guilt for Harry and Mylo that this had taken me away from them. I felt guilt for our immediate family members who were now all having to wonder if they too carried the CF gene.

I carried enough guilt for the world; it was like a dark cloud that hung over me. Every morning I would wake, and then the realisation of what we were living through would hit me and I would feel the dark, heavy cloud return. I was shrouded in guilt, grief and heartache.

Personally, I defy anyone not to feel guilty when their child is in hospital or receives a diagnosis. Whatever the reason they are in there, medical condition or accident, guilt is at the fore. You wish things were different. You wish you could take their pain or ailment and put it onto you, so as to relieve your little one and give them peak health.

I was wracked with guilt those first two months, and to be honest, it was my foremost emotion for two years after. Of course even now when I think about all Bailey endured and the life-long condition he has inherited, I still feel sickeningly guilty that I can't just make it all go away.

I had some of the darkest thoughts ever during the first few months of Bailey's diagnosis, some of which I am ashamed of. When I reflect, I can't believe I felt them, and at the time I felt guilty for allowing them to enter my head, but it was like I couldn't control my own mind. This meant my guilt was tainted with guilt. Never a good place to be.

I know when I had these thoughts and emotions, I spent hours wondering why I was such an awful person. I wasn't sure if anyone else ever felt or thought such things in similar situations, and believing that I was a terrible person added to my upset.

Well if you only take one piece of advice from this entire book please let it be this; it's normal. You're normal, what you're feeling is normal and everyone (I'm almost sure) at one point has felt something similar.

Of course, how long each individual lets those thoughts and feelings stay varies, and how they are impacted and move forward from that differs greatly also.

Yet what I am trying to declare is that all these emotions, however terrible you feel for feeling them, are natural. You are not a bad person. It doesn't mean you don't deserve to have your child. It simply means you're hurting. You feel pain and that's because you love and care for your child, which right now is all you can do for them – and as luck would have it, is the most important thing and the best medicine.

The first thing I've witnessed most parents do after a CF diagnosis is fundraise. They fundraise the heck out of anything; sponsored runs, cake sales, triathlons, selling CF-related attire. Why? Because it's the only darn thing you can do to help.

Parents are powerless; they cannot help their child. Yes, they can administer their medicines and do their physiotherapy, but they cannot heal their baby. They cannot cure their child, so fundraising for a cure is the only option to feel like you're doing anything remotely useful to help – to find the cure you yearn for.

I did it too, running the London marathon and even setting up our own paddle boarding event Stand Up to Cystic Fibrosis (SUP2CF), all raising funds for the CF Trust in a bid to feel like I was helping Bailey and our amazing CF community.

I've witnessed this course of action for many parents with a new medical diagnosis for their child. It's almost a rite of passage. I watch on with empathy as new parents find their innate response to help.

It's a knee-jerk reaction to the situation. All these heartfelt attempts by parents are a way to manage and cope with guilt. The only way they can think of to ease their guilt and helplessness.

As parents, we feel entirely responsible for our child's safety, wellbeing and happiness. You want to give them the most perfect start in life, and yet here you are feeling as if it's anything but.

Guilt is an everyday emotion when you have children. You feel guilty for spending more time with one child than the other, guilty you told them off even though they were in the wrong, guilty for leaving them to go to work or out with friends, guilty for not letting them have their fourth biscuit of the day. You get the idea; feeling guilty is being a parent, my friend.

I know the guilt you feel now is something else altogether and feels darker and heavier than everyday guilt as exampled above. However, you are strong, you will get through and you will find new life stories and happiness to wipe away this incessant emotion.

Guilt is such a powerful sentiment and that feeling is so intense right now. However, I promise it will fade. Maybe not entirely, but I believe we learn to live with it – manage it, perhaps.

I want to tell you not to feel guilty, that none of this is your fault and that this emotion is not valid and won't serve you. However, it doesn't matter how many times people tell you not to feel guilty, it won't ease, so there's not much point me saying any of that.

Instead I advise that you feel, acknowledge and accept your guilt and find your way forward through the pain. It's with you, and fighting it is exhausting.

Guilt will keep you stuck where you are. You need to grow and move forwards, step into your strength and be the most powerful parent to your child. If you still feel you need to do something to help your little one, this is it. Turning your guilt into compassion and strength will help you to heal and allow you to let go of things so you can move forwards and be the parent your child needs.

Feel your guilt. Acknowledge it. Accept it. Know that it's natural. Then allow time to do it's wonderful thing – heal.

How much time, I cannot tell you. What I can tell you is that I no longer wake with that sickening feeling of guilt.

When I look at Bailey and think specifically about his CF, all he went through and all he has to endure each day and everyday thereafter, I feel guilt. It sweeps back over me, feels heavy and dark once more and consumes me. However, it's momentary, because then Bailey smiles or does something ridiculously cute or funny, and that emotion of happiness and love is powerful enough to override my guilt.

Guilt is no longer my dominant daily emotion.

I want to tell you exactly when that changed – the specific day and time, so you know how long it took to reach this point. Yet it wasn't a moment I can pinpoint. It was a gradual fading of guilt and simultaneous growth of happiness as we created moments and memories that were fun-filled and normal.

It occurred as Bailey started to grow and develop into the funny little thing he is, and as I realised that the amazing parts of his life and our family of five would far outweigh the tough parts.

It was when I understood that I didn't know, nor ever had any chance of knowing, that this was going to happen. That I couldn't have done anything differently. That it wasn't my shortcomings or irresponsibility that landed us in the situation. That no matter how much I wanted things to be different, they weren't, so I had to find acceptance and in this acceptance, I could release some of my guilt.

You too have to find acceptance to ease yourself of guilt into forgiveness. I believe that's the point when your guilt diminishes and you give yourself permission to enjoy life whole heartedly once more.

I wasted so much of Bailey's newborn days immersed in guilt, upset, pain, torment and suffering. Please don't waste your precious days.

Guilt is such a powerful emotion. If you don't deal with it, it will hold you back. However, in contrast, overcoming your guilt can help propel you forward to a stronger you. Here's a few tips to help ease yourself of guilt, find forgiveness and move forward into happy moments.

- **Acknowledge it.** Take to your journal and write, "I feel guilty because _____." Let the answers flow from you as explained in the following journal writing chapter. This is just for you and your healing process, so write freely without fear of judgement, so you can move forward from this unfounded feeling.

  Once you've let it all out, from the big to the small, consider if you are at fault? If your friend spoke to you about these feelings of guilt, would you be telling them it wasn't their fault? That they weren't to blame?

- **Say sorry.** Usually, the way we overcome guilt is by apologising to someone, and they accept our apology. If you would like, talk to your child and apologise to them, or write them a letter if you'd prefer. Of course, your child cannot respond, but they don't need to, because they don't need or want your apology. They love you, unconditionally.

- **Forgive yourself.** You have to forgive yourself for not knowing what you did not know before you knew it. I know this is the hardest part of all, but stop being so hard on yourself. Stop hating yourself. You are just a person who wanted a baby. You haven't done anything wrong. You didn't know. It's not your fault, please hear me. Show yourself some compassion. Would you talk to your friend the way you're talking to yourself now, or would you be speaking in your kindest, softest voice telling them to forgive themselves?

CHAPTER 3
Journaling; the why and how

Writing to myself daily while in hospital with Bailey was not something I did to enable me to one day write a book. Quite the opposite, as back then I never could have dreamt I would grow enough to find the strength to share.

I journaled daily as a coping mechanism – a way to allow my thoughts and feelings to flow out, and help make sense of the situation. I wasn't ready to share some of my innermost feelings even to my husband, so by writing them down it was still private, yet enabled me to offload.

I never wrote with any purpose or structure, and I always wrote purely and from the heart, without any fear of judgement as I knew it would never be read by anyone but myself.

I would write every evening, once the day had calmed, visitors had left and Bailey had settled. I would sit down in the infamous arm chair with a peppermint tea and release the day's events and emotions between my pen and paper.

I had never journaled until this point in my life. However, my value for it now has never been stronger. For any parent going through a tough time, whether you're currently in hospital with your child or at home coming to terms with a diagnosis, finding the time to journal will help you through this challenging life phase.

Research proves that journaling can help alleviate anxiety and feelings of depression, help improve your mood and your relationships, and also help you sleep better.[11] Some research even shows that journaling can help improve your immune function and overall wellbeing. At times of upset, it's common to fall unwell due to the stress put on your body, but you simply don't have time to be ill while focusing on your little one. Journal away, dear friend, and let your writing help your health, as well as heal.

---

[11] Smyth JM, Johnson JA, et al, 'Online positive affect journaling in the improvement of mental distress and well-being in general medical patients with elevated anxiety symptoms: A preliminary randomized controlled trial,' *JMIR Mental Health*. 2018;5(4): e11290. doi:10.2196/11290, and Susan Smith et al, The effects of journaling for women with newly diagnosed breast cancer, *Wiley InterScience*, 2005.

On top of this, it helps you make sense of everything at such an unsettling and ever-changing time. Your mind is racing, information is coming at you from all directions and you're trying to keep up with all the new terms and medicines. If you're in hospital, it's often a rollercoaster and sadly you can't get off. You roll with the punches as they lurch at you with each new day. There's no time to compute what's happening, or rationalise it all. Journaling will give you the time and head space to do just this.

I've listed below just a few tips to help you on your journaling journey, in the hope you too can find the benefits of this daily practice.

Write freely

Don't think about what you want to say, whether it makes sense, if your grammar is correct or if it flows well. Just write. It's more of a stream of consciousness. Pick up the pen and write what is heavy on your heart and at the forefront of your mind.

It doesn't matter if it's messy and illegible – this is just for you. It's your outlet and you want your emotions, thoughts and concerns to pour from you so quickly that you can hardly write fast enough.

Let it all out and whatever you want to share with your journal is the right thing. Don't read back over it or edit it – its roughness and rawness is its beauty.

If you have writer's block and simply don't know where to begin, try these prompts to get you flowing:

- Start with the simple sentence, "Today, I feel _____"
- Set yourself a minimum limit, so you have to write for a certain amount of time or fill a specific number of pages. Don't go overboard though as you might feel overwhelmed. Aim with just one page or a couple of minutes to begin with, and once you get going you'll likely far exceed that.
- Write a letter to your child. Not one that will ever be read, but one that you want to write now based on how you feel. Write whatever you want as it is not a letter that will be shared (unless you want it to be).
- Try writing at different times. If you feel too tired to write in the evenings, try in the morning when you first wake up, or during the

day when your child is sleeping, if that works for you. There's no hard and fast rule, so find a rhythm that fits in with your day.

- Treat yourself to a beautiful new notebook and the perfect nib pen in your favourite colour to help you embrace the practice and make it feel like 'you' time. You should want to write in your journal.
- Play some soft, soothing music to help you relax and find your space to write.
- Find a setting or environment that allows you to immerse yourself into your journaling. If you're at home, you can choose any room or quiet nook in the house. If you're in hospital and your child's room just isn't allowing you to let go, find a relaxing coffee shop or quite outside space so you indulge yourself and be undisturbed.
- Writing a physical journal has been found to be most effective, but if pen and paper just isn't your thing, try typing it either on your phone or laptop, or there's a myriad of journaling apps now available. Something is better than nothing, in my opinion.
- If you're not a wordsmith or you find writing challenging in any medium, you could try to express your feelings through art journaling, which is drawing rather than writing.

Write without constraint

Never write worrying that someone might read your journal. If you do, the exercise is wasted as you won't write honestly and purely. If you think it will be read, you will hold back and reserve some of your deepest, darkest thoughts and feelings, which is what this journal is meant for.

Keep your journal somewhere safe and private so you feel safe in writing in your rawest form. You don't even need to tell anyone you are writing it if you don't want to. This is just for you – it's all yours.

Cast your mind back to when you were younger and you perhaps scribbled about someone you fancied or how much your parents were annoying you, or planning your runaway. Perhaps you used to have your book under lock and key, quite literally. You could do the same now if it allows you to feel more comfortable journaling. A book with a lock, or a very safe, secret place to keep it.

The purpose of this journal is to help you in the moment you're writing it. It's future use is of little interest. Even if one day you bin or burn it, that's fine if that allows you to write without any fears or constraints.

Write with thanks

This might feel like a tall ask, but finding at least one thing you are grateful for each day will help you find the positives in an onslaught of negatives. Writing down at least one good thing you experienced is an amazing habit to find appreciation for even the smallest, seemingly insignificant happy things. You can start by just aiming for one thing, but hopefully as time goes on, you might be able to find two, then three, and maybe one day even ten positives.

I didn't do this initially, but I wish I had as I feel certain I could've found one thing each day. I did however complete a gratitude journal each day upon my return home, and continue this practice today.

You might be grateful for your baby's smile, a decent cup of tea or coffee, a positive piece of news from the doctors, a visit from a special friend or sibling, your favourite nurse being on shift, a delicious take away meal, clean bed sheets or simply the sun shining on your walk.

You could also try to identify the positives that have come out of this unexpected life event. A greater appreciation of the small things, a newfound empathy for others in a similar situation who you can perhaps one day support, a realisation of your own true strength, and proof that your health is your wealth, motivating you to invest more into all your family's wellbeing.

I know it can be hard to feel grateful when you are dealt such a raw hand, but finding just one thing is all you have to start with. Just one, then you can grow from there when you feel ready.

CHAPTER 4
Hospital stays; advice for parents and visiting guests
*Written in collaboration with Liana Gomes, fellow parent at
Great Ormond Street Hospital*

One of my biggest blessings from my time at Great Ormond Street Hospital is the friendship I made with another mummy there, Liana, whose daughter Sienna was a patient on the same ward. One of my greatest friendships and biggest inspirations is Liana. We have become friends far beyond the walls of the hospital, and as the powers of the universe would have it, we only live a mere twenty minutes from each other.

I wanted to collaborate with Liana on this section, not because we were both in the same situation, but because our journeys in fact had key differences.

Unlike myself, Liana knew she would be going to GOSH when Sienna was delivered, because her exomphalos (also known as omphalocele) was cited and diagnosed at a pregnancy scan. Given Liana also had another newborn, Sienna's twin sister Ariella, plus three boys at home, Lorenzo, Valentino and Tiago, she was unable to stay in the hospital full time like I did. Liana could therefore also offer valuable advice on preparing for a planned post-birth hospital stay, while sharing her time between home and hospital.

Hospital stays take their toll on the parents, emotionally, mentally and even physically. We want to impart some of our key learnings to help you survive your time in the four walls. Equally though, these situations are challenging for visitors and loved ones, too. Knowing what to say, do and bring are all common concerns. So we also share some tips, ideas and advice that we found valuable from those around us offering support and love. Therefore, we've created two sections to this chapter;

1. Advice for parents in hospital with their child
2. Advice for visiting friends and family

1. Advice for parents in hospital with their child

Give yourself time

When Liana and I composed this section of the book, we did so sat on a cold park bench with a blanket and cup of tea in the midst of one of the UK's national lockdowns, reminiscing on all we had learnt from our shared experiences over three years ago. This is the first time we managed to speak about it all without one of us crying. So whatever advice we offer you here, please know that our biggest piece of advice is to give yourself *time*.

How much time? Only time will tell, but one thing we know for sure is that it will take time – likely time far beyond your days within the confines of the hospital walls. Time to heal, to accept, to grieve, to reflect and to grow.

In hindsight, I wish I'd given myself more time and lots more grace. I feel sorry for that woman who was trying so hard to continue to be all to everyone, despite her own grief and pain. I wasn't ready and I probably should have continued to hide away and protect myself and heal. Yet my bid to do normal things and maintain normality for the boys was such that it drove me to pretend I was ready. I was so far from ready.

It is one of my biggest learnings that I hope other parents take away and implement. Don't feel guilty for doing it either. The days after having a baby are hazy, and the days after receiving a diagnosis for your baby are even hazier. That first whole year is a sleep-deprived, grief-stricken blur for me. I should have been curled up in my safe place, not wandering the streets at a loss.

So whatever your journey, give yourself time and grace, and once you think you've healed, give yourself a little more time. It's probably only the first layer of skin that's healed. Your wounds are likely to be deep and it will take more than a delicate scab to mask over some of your pain without it re-emerging.

Neither Liana nor I feel we are the same person today as the women who first went into our personal experiences. While yes, the condition or ailment belongs to your child, there is nothing more heart-breaking than watching your little one go through these helpless situations. You will want to take it all away, but you can't my friend. If only we could.

Don't try to do everything yourself
You are going to need help from friends and family, fact. Just accept it. Whether you have other children already or not, you can't do everything by yourself. Asking for help is important and will see you through this challenging time. Don't be embarrassed to ask – you're not a burden and people genuinely want to help in the best way they can so they will be pleased you asked. And if they offer, accept graciously.

Home preparation
Whether you know you are going in to hospital beforehand, or it hits you out of nowhere, one thing we both know is the importance of being prepared and organised at home.

For those with other children, having childcare sorted is a load off your mind. If you know you'll be going in to hospital, pre-plan all your children's care, play dates and pick-ups for the first two to three weeks.

If you're admitted unexpectedly, scrape together a week's worth of childcare as best you can. From there, plan where they will be when on a weekly basis, so you've got it all sorted and you're not worrying about it day-to-day.

Having a concise childcare schedule, perhaps written out so you can clearly see it at a glance, is very important so you can be present with your baby. It's also important to clearly explain to the children the plan of the week verbally so they have an outline of their days, even if they don't remember all the finer details. You could put a poster of their schedule on the wall for them to refer to so they know where they are going, when.

Of course, a freezer full of prepared homemade meals is a dream. Batch cook and separate into individual servings that can be defrosted and heated with ease for the family. Equally though, if you've not had time, a few ready meals for those at home are fine for now if it relieves the pressure. Don't set your standards too high – right now you need to keep life as simple as possible. You can worry about getting some wholesome food into them later.

Online shops are a lifesaver in these situations. You can shop and book the delivery from hospital, while the adult at home can simply receive the food and unpack.

Everyday tasks such as cooking and shopping can feel so tiresome and inconvenient when you have so much going on. Sharing the load and making life as simple as possible is the best way forward.

Bag packing

Whether you're packing in advance, or throwing some bits together in a frenzied rush, we picked up some great ideas of some essentials you might not think of between the normal stuff of nappies and night clothes. If you had to hurry to hospital, ask friends or family to bring in some of these items while you're staying on the ward.

We've also included some ideas for when your child is older, should regular hospital admissions be a possibility for them longer term.

- **Comforters** – Sometimes you might not be able to hold your baby, so a teddy or comforter can provide your tiny person exactly that; comfort. They're also a great little trick to prop up tubes so they stay in place and are soft against babies' delicate skin.

  Take more than one, so you can have one and they can have one. Keep yours tucked into your top so it lays on your chest. It will make the comforter smell of you, while your baby's will smell of them. Every so often, swap them over as a way to make you feel close, plus it can help soothe baby as they can smell their mummy.

  You can do it with dads and siblings too, so you all feel connected. I also did it with my bigger two boys while we were apart; we each had our own little knitted square that GOSH gave us. We used to sleep with it every night and when we saw each other we would swab our knitted squares. It's a way to feel close to anyone you can't be near or hold.

- **Your own pillow** – Sleep is the best medicine for you all, so make sure you sleep as well as you can between being woken. You might also want to bring your own blanket and/or sleeping bag for them, as well as you. Creature comforts really will make all the difference.

- **Reading material** – There's a lot of time to kill, and reading helps avoid scrolling on your phone, usually social media, which often won't serve you in these situations (more on that coming up). You might want a fictional book to escape your current reality and provide a breath of fresh air, or a self-development book might prove useful to give you the tools and mindset to help you through this time.

- **Reading light** – A little reading light is ideal if you want to sit and read or journal in the evenings while your child sleeps, but without the harsh glare of the hospital room lights.

- **Travel mug** – Tea and coffee tastes much nicer in your own mug than out of the small, plastic cups, plus you get a lot more, too.

- **Slippers** – At least you'll feel relatively cosy in the evenings when you settle down. You don't want to be walking around the ward barefoot, trust us.

- **Laptop/iPad** – Great entertainment for all of you, from watching programmes to playing games, or even working.

- **Sanitising wipes** – Great to keep all your toys clean, plus wiping down any tables in your room.

- **Snacks for you and your child** – This gives you some control between their set hospital meal times and means they can still enjoy your daily favourites. Bring some for you too, ranging from healthy to well-earned treats.

- **Toys/games/colouring** – Days can be long, so ensure your little one and any visiting siblings, are entertained. Many hospitals have play rooms or even a play team, but it never hurts to have your own supplies on tap, too.

- **A play mat for the floor** – Ideally one you can wipe down with Dettol, rather than a fabric one. This gives them a play spot other than just their cot.

- **Photos** – Bring your family, friends and fun times into the hospital. Decorate their space with these special people and memories so they don't feel so far away. You can also decorate with sibling drawings.

- **Fitness clothes and trainers** – Whether you want to keep up your running training or let off steam on a power walk, you'll want some active wear available. It works wonders for the mindset and stops the walls closing in on you completely.

- **Good quality frozen ready meals** – Most hospitals have a kitchen area where you can microwave these if you tire of the canteen offerings.

- **Moisture aid** – Lip balm and body moisturiser, both for children and parents, are must-haves due to the constant air con that dries out skin.

- **Online deliveries** – remember, you can order online and have it delivered to you in hospital if you don't have something you need. Many hospitals now have Amazon Hub Lockers for drop off points, which is so useful when you've forgotten something.

Lastly, but most importantly, **don't neglect packing for you.** Self-care for you during this time is going to prove so important. No, we're not joking. We know this feels like the completely inappropriate time to be worrying about these things and it's far from the most relaxing of settings, but that's not what we mean.

Don't let yourself go completely, otherwise you risk losing yourself. You need to do the small daily actions you often do to make yourself feel ready for the day, from brushing your teeth to having some nice smellies.

Rather than pack the cheap free minis you've got lurking at the bottom of your toiletry drawer, take in the gorgeous smelling shower gel and your usual haircare. Goodness, even take in your favourite perfume. It's not about how you look in there; it's about how you *feel*. By following your usual daily habits, you will feel more like you.

Erase that sentiment of guilt or vanity about doing something for you and gift yourself these small, yet significant things. Right now the most important thing is to be strong and your wellbeing will see you through this journey, and this is one small step you can do to help you on your way.

It doesn't just have to be toiletries either. Whatever is going to make you feel more human, stronger and in control of you, pack it.

Take each day as it comes

Don't make any definite plans or set any certain homecoming dates in your head. The whole process is unknown until it happens. Even if you know before your baby is born that they will have a hospital stay, the specialists won't be able to tell you for definite how things will go exactly, nor how long your child will be in for.

Once anyone finds themselves in hospital, things can change daily, if not hourly. You might be going home one minute, and the next there's no end in sight. You don't want to set yourself up for a potential downfall, so just focus on the next twenty-four hours. Take each step as it comes and take the whole journey one day at a time. Don't look too far ahead, otherwise the overwhelm will hit you. One day, then the next, then the next. You've got this, dear mumma.

Don't search online

Jumping onto Google to research your child's condition is not going to serve you. Yes, there are hours of time to fill while on long hospital stays, but in contrast, you have doctors aplenty at your disposal.

Speak directly with your child's specialist team who can give you all the accurate advice you need and direct you to validated resources on the web. Not only is there inaccurate and scaremongering information out there, but everyone's journey will be different.

Sharing your news and social media

Wow, this really is a personal one, and something that's difficult to address in any finite way.

At some point, you need to accept that you are going to have to start telling people of your plight. When and how you do this is totally up to you, but the most important overriding message, is to do what you feel comfortable.

Liana knew before delivery that Sienna would be going to hospital after her birth, so she took the opportunity to tell her sons and close family, but she didn't tell many friends about what awaited her on the other side of the twins' delivery.

I only told a few close friends we had unexpectedly been admitted to hospital, and that was almost a week after being there. I simply couldn't process, accept or share prior to this.

Who, when and what you tell people will be totally down to you, your personality and how you feel each day. You will know when you're ready to share, and with whom. You will know that some people will be good for you, while others won't help in this situation, so it might be the case that you want to let some people in and not others.

Sharing on social media platforms is also a very personal choice. Some people will feel comfortable documenting their entire journey in a bid to gain support and raise awareness. It's likely a cathartic process – a bit like journaling, only it's for the world to see rather than private. It can be a great coping tool, but only if it's the right path for you.

Social media is a great way to keep everyone up to date without having to send multiple personal messages with the same information, and can be such a great campaign to increase knowledge of lesser-known conditions.

However, some people will want to keep their painful journey private. They perhaps don't want their child to be public property or they simply might not feel strong enough to take on the onslaught of concerned questions and comments.

I kept our journey off social media until we got home. I did post a few images of Bailey over the nine-week hospital stay, but each one looked like he could've been at home. There was no tell-tale sign in the images that he was in hospital, and this was a conscious decision to avoid a barrage of questions I wasn't yet ready to receive or equipped to answer. That was over two months of secrecy, which proves how easy it is to 'lie' on social media, so maybe there's a lesson for us all there.

Ultimately, it is totally up to you and what you feel comfortable with, but one thing's for sure; stick to what you're happy with. Only share when you're ready and only tell those you want to. Don't feel under any pressure or worry about anybody's feelings. You have to focus on yourself and what works for you and if that means feeling selfish, then so be it. If sharing helps, then go for it. If it's not serving you, then keep it within a smaller circle of loved ones.

Sibling hospital visits

This always sounds like an idyllic event, but it can actually be quite stressful. The children are trying to touch everything and you might feel on edge, worrying about whether they're going to pull something out, or cause too much noise and commotion for others on the ward. First and foremost though, all they want is to meet their new brother or sister, so allow them to forge that bond.

- **Let them in** – One thing's for sure is that you have to let the other children into the situation. If you know in advance, forewarn them before the baby arrives that he/she will be in hospital for a while and mummy and/or daddy might not be around as much. It will give them time to get their head around it all, just like you.

  Until you feel able to let the children visit in person, chat to them on the phone, and when you feel ready, use video calls. This lets them see you, the baby and your surroundings and makes them feel more familiar with what's going on and like they are with you. You might not feel strong enough to speak or see the other children for a few days or a week or so, but don't give yourself a hard time about this. You've got to do what's right for you. Nothing is wrong in these situations; it's about finding ways to cope and what works for you.

- **Keep visits short** – Two to three hours is plenty. If the siblings are young, they will take one look at their baby, say hi and then want something to entertain them. This would be slightly different for older brothers and sisters, but let's be honest, there's not much to do in hospitals.

- **Pack things to do** – On that note, be sure to bring electronics, colouring and snacks. Some hospitals, such as GOSH, have an arts and toys room so they can go for a play in there or visit an onsite play area. If you're able to leave the hospital with baby, maybe they could push them in the pram to a nearby playground so they feel they are spending time with their new sibling, but you're also getting them out to run off some energy.

Relationships with fellow parents

When you undergo long hospital stays, it's inevitable that you might get to know the family in the cubicle next to you, or see the same faces around the corridors and kitchen.

Depending on your character type and how you're fairing, will depend if you would find it beneficial, and are indeed open, to forming friendships with parents in the hospital.

Liana, knowing she was due to go in to GOSH, was offered by her doctor to be partnered up with someone in the same situation as her. Although she didn't follow this path, she was most definitely the social one on our ward. She was open to meeting new people, forging conversations and got to know lots of the families on the ward.

I, in stark contrast, was not at all open to speaking to anyone other than Bailey's team and my visiting friends and family. I didn't engage with anyone. I was hurting too much and I could hardly compose a sentence to someone I knew, let alone someone I didn't. Yet, perhaps speaking to someone you don't know might sometimes actually be easier?

It is only Liana that I got to know well, because she was so open and friendly, and the universe I believe brought us together.

However, it's true that nobody will understand exactly what you are going through except for another parent who has been through the same.

It was so wonderful to have at least one person to speak to so you can exchange thoughts, worries, vent without judgement and cry with their complete empathy. You can describe to your friends on the outside world what has happened in your journey. You could tell them every tiny detail if they are happy to listen. However, nobody will ever fully understand the emotional rollercoaster you're on and the depth of some of your emotions, apart from those who are in there with you.

Speaking to those on the 'inside' can be cathartic and make you feel totally understood and like you're not going crazy or being judged for any of your thoughts. You can share more honestly with those who understand more. Liana and I could often be found sat by one of our baby's bedsides having a cuppa and a chat after a particularly stressful day. It really can be so valuable, but finding the right person is very important.

Feeding

As mums, you don't need us to tell you the ongoing discussions around breastfeeding, but whatever your take and experience on this topic, we felt the need to say something on it due to our different situations.

Liana was toing and froing from hospital, with three other children to care for and another newborn to feed. When she was with Sienna, she breastfed her because she was breastfeeding her twin sister Ariella anyway, so the milk was there. When Liana was back at home, the nurses fed Sienna her bottle of formula.

However, over time, the stress of juggling five children, commuting to London and breastfeeding was just too much. Plus, Sienna's doctors actually recommended it would better suit Sienna's gut to stick to just one type of milk. Liana switched to formula and stopped breastfeeding altogether. You want to make your life as manageable as possible, and also cut yourself some slack in areas that you can simplify.

In contrast, I wasn't allowed to breastfeed Bailey most of the time, so my only option if I wanted him to ever breastfeed again was to continually express my milk, which I did.

I had lost all control in the blink of an eye and having the goal of being able to breastfeed again became something to focus on and strive for. I wanted to take on the task, and given I was sat around the hospital for the majority of the time with a breast pump to hand, it was easy enough. In many ways, it added structure to my days as I had to stick to a time schedule.

As with most of our experience and advice, do what's right for you. Don't put yourself under pressure to breastfeed if it's adding stress and upset to your situation. You're already in a distressing situation, so it might just not be something you want to add into the mix. Accept that and let go. A fed baby is all that counts.

Equally, if breastfeeding provides you the closeness you crave to your baby and makes you feel like you're fulfilling part of your mummy role, go for it. Even if people around you are telling you not to worry, if it's something you want to do for you and baby, that's up to you. If so, read our advice from breastfeeding and expressing specialist Caroline Jordan in chapter 5.

The pros to bottle feeding are that it allows a more accurate account of how much milk baby has drunk – with breastfeeding there's no way of knowing so it's more difficult to gauge.

Of course, always follow the advice from your child's medical consultant. We are just talking about it from a personal standpoint.

Focus on you

If you don't want visitors, cancel. If you don't want to share certain information, don't.

Throughout this journey you need to focus on your baby and you. You can't be taking on anyone else's feelings right now. If you want to cancel someone, just be honest and polite. If they love you, they will understand entirely.

How you are mentally and emotionally will change from one day to the next, one hospital event to the next. Allow yourself to move with your evolving story.

Do what feels right for you in that moment, and don't waste energy feeling guilty about it. You are on a unique journey and right now the only right and wrong is determined by what helps and supports you.

Have comfort that with each day and experience, you will grow. You will learn and become stronger, and the more experienced you become, things will start to feel more normal and less overwhelming. With each stage you will feel a little more knowing and a little more confident, so go on and grow mumma, and shine your love and light to your baby.

2. Advice for visiting friends and family

Since our stay in Great Ormond Street Hospital, so many friends have asked us for advice on what to do to help others who have since found themselves in this challenging situation.

While words can be such a comfort, often people simply don't know what to say. If that's the case, there are a host of simple acts of kindness and thoughtfulness, which can be hugely valuable and helpful. Here's our advice to help those visiting guests.

Visiting

Visit when you can, but don't be offended if they cancel on the day. Events evolve quickly in hospitals, and they can't predict what one day will bring. Plus, they're always waiting on the arrival of busy doctors, and the reality is that this is far more important than a kind visitor.

If you can't visit due to your own work and family commitments, keep in touch. Send a thoughtful message, but again, don't be upset or worried if they don't answer straight away. We always caught up on messages in the evenings when things were calm and quiet.

Voice notes in particular are a winner as they are so personal; they can hear your caring tone and the sound of a familiar voice at such strange times offers huge comfort.

What to say

Sometimes your friend might want to talk about all that's going on in their hospital world, while other times they might want to chat about something mundane, such as some school gate chat or new TV show. How do you know? Ask.

Kindly and gently ask what they would like to talk about. Something along the lines of, "How are you feeling today? Would you like to talk about it all, because if so I am here to listen? But if you want to talk about something completely different, then I'm happy to distract you with some mundane gossip."

Just always remember, many of your questions will likely be their questions. If you aren't chatting all things hospital, try to make them laugh with your other news. The endorphins will do them wonders and when you leave they will feel lifted from your visit.

Congratulate

When you see the parents for the first time following the baby's arrival, say congratulations. Whatever situation they sadly find themselves in, don't let that overshadow the fact they have a new child. No matter what the reason their baby is in hospital, they still love and adore their little one unconditionally and feel they are utterly beautiful and perfect and want to be congratulated on their new addition.

So many times people begin with, "I'm so sorry". Although this is so well intended, it is quite negative and upsetting – right now they need to be bolstered up with positivity. Coo over the baby, just as you would in more normal circumstances, but equally show an interest in understanding the situation and seeing how they're doing. A fine balance, we appreciate.

Meals

If you're visiting, don't take flowers; these are seldom allowed and home cooked food is far more gratefully received. There was nothing quite like some healthy, nutritious, homemade food so you don't need to dine on the canteen offerings, again. Ideally something they can heat up in the microwave, or a Tupperware of nice biscuits or even just a selection of fruit and healthy snacks.

Pamper SOS

The parents are often overlooked in these situations as they and everyone else is so focused on the baby. Usually the mother feels rotten; she's not had a bath in ages, her beauty regime is non-existent and the last thing she is concerned with is her own wellbeing.

For new mums, remember they have still just had a baby. Of course they still have the endorphin high of the gift of a new little one, but let's be honest, mainly you feel horrendous, like you've been hit by a bus and then need to get up and walk home.

So imagine experiencing all the new-mum feels and all the unglamorous bodily functions, while watching your newborn in hospital. Everything you normally experience in the comfort of your own home is now being done in a hospital bathroom with hundreds of people coming and going. They're leaking out of every orifice and they feel like death warmed up, but tripled as they are also going through a trauma.

It's easy to forget when the patient is the baby, but this mumma would ordinarily have been feet up in bed or on the sofa, being cooked nutritious dinners and run hot baths. Right now, the last person in the world she is thinking of is herself.

If there's a beauty salon nearby, why not treat her to a manicure or pedicure, and offer to sit with their baby while she goes? Perhaps even a haircut or blow dry, or bring in some beauty products that she can enjoy.

As vain as it sounds, we recall the heels of our feet were harder than they've ever been, and Liana and I often said the first thing we were going to do to celebrate our babies coming home was treat ourselves to a pedicure.

Unexpected surprises

Doing small thoughtful acts of kindness for your friends right now will feel like the grandest gesture for them.

Maybe write a letter and post it to them – there's nothing like receiving a card in the post at a hospital. You could send a little gift box or some biscuits. If you can't be there in person, let them know you're thinking about them. It will brighten up an otherwise monotonous day.

Perhaps record a little video message of yourself and WhatsApp it to them so they get to see and hear you even if they don't feel much like talking yet. It's a connection to their normal world outside of hospital.

You could organise an event for them to look forward to once home. Don't set a date as they likely have no idea when they'll return home, but perhaps have an occasion such as a spa day, golf day, afternoon tea, lunch with a group of friends or a great bike ride in the countryside. Just something you can talk about and they can focus on – something that your friend will enjoy and be excited by.

CHAPTER 5
Expressing to breastfeeding; support at times of distress
Written in collaboration with Caroline Jordan, Infant Feeding Specialist Midwife and Lactation Consultant (IBCLC)

One of the very first things that might happen if your baby is admitted to hospital, is that the doctors may choose to make them nil by mouth. This means your baby can no longer consume milk, while the specialists carry out checks and procedures. For those mums wishing to breastfeed, this can pose a problem as you need to feed to keep your milk supply up. Say a very warm hello to your friend, the breast pump.

OK, so in truth you will get sick of the sight of it soon enough, but if it means you can even attempt to maintain milk supply for when your baby is ready, then it's worth it.

Bailey was off milk for almost two months. I expressed every three hours, every single day. I woke nightly to mimic my baby's night feed. I sat attached to that yellow Medela pump for so many hours that in the end the nurses just left a permanent one in our room to save me rolling it to and from the expressing area.

I hated that yellow Medela pump. In my mind, I can see it clearly to this day. However, I love it too, because thanks to that very clever machine, I was able to return to breastfeeding after a long time apart from Bailey.

I absolutely know how fortunate I am that I have always had a good milk supply for all three of my boys, so perhaps that put me in good stead. I am acutely aware that some women, no matter how hard they try and through no fault of their own, simply won't be able to maintain milk supply, whether breastfeeding or expressing. All hail the wonder that is baby milk formula.

However, what I do believe is that with the right advice – the advice we have put together for you here – many mummies at least have a fighting chance of keeping your supply in full flow while baby is helped by their care team.

It won't work for everyone, and if you simply can't produce the milk or it's causing you too much stress, please for the love of yourself, stop. Do not beat yourself up about it, and don't feel like you've failed. These are not normal circumstances, and expressing at the best of times is challenging.

Expressing while you're going through such tough times is even harder. Don't add to your stressful load if it's not working for you.

I often used to sit with my yellow Medela pump, sobbing as it sucked away at my breast like I was a cow being milked. I was crying my heart out during my hardest time, and I expected my body to perform. Crazy really, given milk supply relies on the happy hormone oxytocin.

For me however, this was the one thing I felt I could do for Bailey – a way to stay in control when everything else was taken away and continue to be his mother by giving him something nobody else could. It also gave my day structure and purpose.

So many nurses told me to stop and so many people thought I was crazy for persisting. Every time I carried another full bottle to the nurses' station for them to put in the growing freezer collection, they looked at me both disbelieving and sympathetically for continuing in my expressing mission.

During National Breastfeeding Week in August, after almost eight weeks of expressing and several days before Bailey successfully breastfed once more, I donated 150 bottles to the St Guys and Thomas milk bank for the Neonatal Unit.

I knew Bailey would never be able to drink all this milk, plus it was taking up two large freezer drawers on our ward at GOSH, which they wanted emptied. I trusted in me to express, and I trusted in Bailey to breastfeed again when he could, and he did, which meant we didn't need all my expressed milk. The milk was simply a by-product of the purpose my expressing was serving; to maintain milk supply manually while unable to breastfeed.

Something good had to come of this situation, and this was me giving back after all the love and care Bailey received. My hope is that those bottles of nutritious breastmilk made their way to the most special neonatal babies and made some difference to their health, while hopefully offering some comfort to their mummies.

I honestly don't tell you this to boast. I tell you to give you hope and to show you what's possible. I tell you so that you believe in you, and know that sometimes – just sometimes – your maternal love and strength outweighs some of the advice you may receive. Trust that you can do this, if you wish to.

If you do want to one day breastfeed again or you're able to give baby controlled, measured bottles of expressed milk as instructed by their doctors, let's take a deep dive into the advice from Caroline Jordan, the very lady that helped me while expressing. We cover techniques, timings, monitoring your schedule with chocolate squares, making baby feel close when they're not near and returning to breastfeeding after time apart.

For those mummas who are still able to breastfeed their baby while in hospital, my hope is that you too might find some helpful tips about keeping milk production up during upsetting times.

There is, of course, so much information available online, so we've included some useful and reliable website links in the footnotes, so you can visit those resources should you wish, and listed a range of specialist in-person support available to you also.

Expressing 101

If possible, start expressing as soon as you learn that you're no longer able to breastfeed your baby. This will ensure messages are still sent to the brain that the body needs to continue to produce milk.

The brain releases the hormone prolactin, which stimulates the milk cells to produce milk, and oxytocin, which delivers the milk by squeezing the muscle layer around each milk cell. The milk moves from the milk cells into the milk ducts to the nipple and, in this case, to the pump.

It's very important to express in the early weeks, because it will determine your future milk supply. Long-term milk supply is based on the frequency of breastfeeds/expressions in the early days after baby is born, when prolactin receptor sites on the milk cells are switched on and activated.

After birth, breast milk supply/production is controlled by the hormones oxytocin and prolactin. Later on it changes to a local milk removal control, sometimes known as the Feedback Inhibitor of Lactation (FIL). A protein in the milk acts as a gatekeeper and matches supply to demand. It needs to be removed either by the baby feeding or by expressing.

When the milk is removed from the breast, this will signal that more milk needs to be made. If the milk is not removed, milk supply may decrease as FIL will stop the milk hormones being released and send a message to the brain that less milk is needed.

If your newborn baby is unable to breastfeed from birth, start by hand expressing as soon as possible and definitely by the time your baby is 6 hours old to switch on the prolactin receptors in the milk cells, which helps with your long-term milk production.

Hand expressing is the best way to collect colostrum – the first milk your breasts produce. It's sometimes referred to as 'liquid gold', because it contains antibodies to protect against infection, kicks start the immune system, coats the gut and acts as a laxative to help baby pass the first sticky dark stool, called meconium. A video guide to hand expressing can be found at Global Health Media.[12]

Your breast milk is unique to both you and your baby, so be proud of every drop you produce. However, if you are struggling to produce milk, you could try mixed feeding. This is a combination of formula and breast milk, which continues to offer the health benefits. First Steps Nutrition provides information on all types of milk and infant feeding.[13]

Expressing frequency and duration

Try to mimic your baby's current feeding pattern as best you can. This will ensure your milk supply is stimulated and your production is maintained for your baby when they're able to breastfeed again.

A newborn baby breastfeeds at least 8-12 times every 24 hours, so aim to express at least 8-10 times in each 24-hour period. These sessions do not need to be evenly spaced, however it will help preserve your milk supply if you avoid gaps of longer than 4 hours during the day and 6 hours at night.

It's important to express during the night, because prolactin, the hormone that stimulates the milk cells to make breast milk, is higher at this time. Set an alarm during the night to wake you while you sleep – just like your baby would do.

A useful rule of thumb for how long to express at each session is no longer than a breastfeed, which may vary widely from 5-40 minutes, depending on how fast your milk flows and your baby's suckle.

If you're using a single pump, express for 20-30 minutes or double pump for 10-15 minutes, or for several minutes after the last drops of milk are expressed.

Do use your breasts as a guide and stop pumping when your breasts feel softer and comfortable, rather than just watching the clock.

The Unicef Expressing Assessment can be a great support when expressing.[14] You can complete it by yourself, with your partner or with the health professional caring for you and your baby.

---

[12] Visit https://globalhealthmedia.org then go to Videos and choose Small Baby.
[13] Visit www.firststeps.nutrition.org.
[14] Visit www.unicef.org.uk.

While expressing frequently in the early days will ensure milk production later on, you may find after a while you can reduce the number of times you express whilst still obtaining the same volume of milk in 24 hours. Some mums may reduce from 8 expressing episodes down to 6.

Women will usually produce the same amount of milk in a 24-hour period (approximately 700mls-750mls by day 14). However, the storage capacity in their breasts may vary and this is not always indicated by breast size. One mum may express 6 times in 24 hours and the other may need to express 8-10 times in order to get the same volume of milk for her baby.

It may be helpful to think about your 'magic number'.[15] This is how often you need to remove milk from your breasts each day to maintain your milk production. If the number of times you remove milk dips below your magic number, your milk supply may slow down. This is affected by breast fullness and breast storage capacity. Breast fullness can slow milk production, whereas an empty breast produces milk more quickly than a full one.

Some mums find it helps to eat a square or two of dark chocolate before they express. La Leche suggest placing 8-10 sweets or chocolate next to your pump and to eat one every time you express. This is a fun way to keep track of your daily expressing schedule and by the end of the day they should all be eaten, meaning you've had some much-needed extra calories too.

Expressing at times of distress

Try not to panic if you are unable to produce much milk the first time you try expressing. Firstly, you're likely feeling upset and stressed, which can inhibit the flow of oxytocin, and in turn slow down your milk flow.

Secondly, babies are much more efficient at transferring milk from their mums' breasts than an expressing pump, so give yourself time to practice this new skill.

Oxytocin is often called the love or feel good hormone, so think about what helps you relax and try this before you next express. Listening to music or a podcast, reading, watching TV or chatting to friends and family may help you relax and distract you. A massage or having your hair brushed may also help.

---

[15] To learn more about the Magic Number visit
http://www.nancymohrbacher.com/articles/tag/Magic+Number.

Having your baby near to you or giving them a skin-to-skin cuddle if you're able, will also help release the breastfeeding hormones. However, you may find it challenging to hold baby safely and express at the same time. Plus, baby may instinctively try to latch on and breastfeed, so it's a case of experimenting and finding out what works for you.

If you cannot hold or be with your baby, watch a video or look at photos of them while you express. Simply holding an unwashed babygro, muslin or bonding heart (a piece of material sewn into a heart shape for this exact purpose) that smells of them so you can feel close will also help. Swap your item regularly between baby and yourself to ensure both your scents don't fade.

Applying warmth to your breasts will encourage the let-down reflex, so often having a warm shower or bath before you express can help. You could try applying warm flannels, wheat pillows or gel breast pads that can be heated up before you express.

Lightly massage your breasts before you start expressing to help increase the hormones. You could also try hand expressing to get the milk flowing before you use the breast pump.

Always remember, every drop of your breast milk is precious, so value however much you are able to express. You are the only person who can produce your baby's unique breast milk, so always be kind and take care of yourself.[16]

Different breasts, different milk volumes

It's very normal and common that one breast produces more milk than the other side. Primarily, our bodies aren't symmetrical and often one breast is larger than the other. Plus, the amount of milk cells, ducts and storage capacity also varies between breasts.

If you're right handed you may find it is easier to position your baby on your left breast, and in turn may have unknowingly developed a preference for one side.

You can help the other side produce more milk by expressing more on that side to stimulate more milk. An empty breast produces milk more quickly than a full one, so the more often you express can help to increase your milk supply.

---

[16] Visit https://www.nct.org.uk/reasonstobeproud.

Expressing techniques

1. Double pumping

Expressing from both breasts at the same time will reduce the time you spend on the pump by 50%. Research by Riordan has shown that this technique also increases the volume expressed by 18%, as it stimulates another let-down reflex during the pumping session.

A let-down or milk ejection reflex happens when the baby has started suckling and messages are sent from the nerves in the breast to the mum's brain to release oxytocin, the hormone that delivers the milk.

The milk from double pumping will also have a higher fat content as more milk is removed from the breast, because the higher fat milk droplets that stick to the milk cells and ducts will be collected.

It can take a while to get used to double pumping and holding both pumping sets in place. Some mums adapt a sports bra by cutting a circle in the middle of the cup area to hold the pump shield/flanges in place and are then hands free.

Single pump expressing from one breast and then switching to the other breast may take longer and you may not produce as much milk. However, some women prefer the single pump method as they can hold the set with one hand and massage the breast and use breast compressions with the other, which can help increase the milk flow.[17]

If single pumping is your preference, express from one breast for 5 minutes and swap to the other side for 5 minutes, then swap back to the first breast and repeat, so each breast is pumped twice.

2. Cluster Pumping

Express every hour for 10 minutes for 6 hours.

Cluster pumping is a useful strategy to increase your supply and to catch up on expressing. It replicates cluster feeding, when the baby breastfeeds frequently with a short space between feeds in a cluster pattern. This is often in the evening and sometimes coincides with a growth spurt.

---

[17] For tips on hand compressions, visit https://realbabymilk.org/breastcompression.

3. Power Pumping

Express for 20 minutes, rest for 10 minutes, express for 10 minutes, rest for 10 minutes, express for 10 minutes, rest for 10 minutes.

You will be expressing 3 times in an hour, and emptying your breasts will send the message to your body that more milk needs to be made. You can count this as one of your 8-10 expressing episodes.

Foods and supplements to aid milk production

You do not have to eat or drink anything special to make breast milk, although it is important to eat a healthy diet. At times of distress, you might not feel like eating much, but it's essential to keep your energy levels up.[18]

You may find that you're suddenly thirsty when you are breastfeeding or expressing, so listen to your body and have some water to hand.

- **Vitamin D supplements** of 10mcgs a day are recommended for the whole UK population including pregnant, breastfeeding women and breastfed babies from birth (Vitamin D is added to formula milk). This is due to the risk of Vitamin D deficiency from the lack of sunlight in the autumn and winter months. The body creates Vitamin D from sunlight and from certain foods, such as oily fish, red meat, mushrooms, egg yolks, fortified cereals and fat spreads.[19]

- **Galactagogues** are foods and herbal or pharmaceutical substances that are believed to increase milk production and supply. Traditional world cultures have prepared special foods for thousands of years to enhance a new mother's milk supply. Some of these foods include;
  o Grains – barley, oatmeal, oats and cornmeal
  o Wholegrain rice
  o Nuts and seeds – almonds, sesame seeds, pumpkin and sunflower seeds

---

[18] For NHS advice on a healthy diet, visit
https://www.nhs.uk/conditions/baby/breastfeeding-and-bottle-feeding/breastfeeding-and-lifestyle/diet/.
[19] Read more information on vitamin D online at
https://www.breastfeedingnetwork.org.uk/vitamind/ and
https://www.nhs.uk/conditions/vitamins-and-minerals/vitamin-d/.

- o   Fruit and vegetables - fennel, anise, papaya and coconut
- o   Herbs – fenugreek and moringa

You can access recipes online for lactation teas/cookies that contain many of the above ingredients, but there is no official evidence to demonstrate that eating a particular food or drink will increase your supply.[20]

Sometimes herbal remedies such as fenugreek and drugs (such as Domperidone) are taken/prescribed to increase milk supply. These should only be considered after you have received skilled support and have followed a plan to increase and maintain your milk supply.[21]

Returning to breastfeeding

So you've spent all this time keeping your milk supply up and ready for when baby can breastfeed once more. First of all, if you're at this point, a huge congratulations to you.

You've worked hard during a challenging time to achieve this. Now it's time to help your baby find their latch again after time off the breast, and there are several things you can do to help your little one.

- A breast (or boob) moon is when baby has unrestricted access to your breasts. This helps encourage your baby to breastfeed again, getting them used to the smell and feel of your breasts and let them navigate their way to the breast and nipple.

- Spend time relaxing with your baby, having skin-to-skin cuddles and enjoying baths together. You may find it helpful to carry your baby in a sling with your breasts uncovered (no bra), so that your breasts are available to your baby.

- If you have been giving your baby expressed breast milk in a bottle, start giving it during skin-to-skin, with you lying in a laid back position at a 45-degree angle.

---

[20] Suggestions and recipes can be found at https://www.lowmilksupply.org.
[21] Visit the Breastfeeding Network Drug Fact Sheets for further information https://www.breastfeedingnetwork.org.uk/drugs-factsheets/.

- When a baby is born they go through instinctive stages and behaviours, including touching the breast and nipple with their hands, licking and nuzzling the areola and nipple, sucking briefly and then latching on. Your baby may start to show some of these signs straightaway, or they might take a while to work out what to do, so it's a case of being patient and celebrating each sign as a step towards breastfeeding again.

- Try hand expressing some milk onto the end of your nipple and areola so that they can smell and lick the breast milk and start to re-associate breast milk and feeding with your breasts.[22]

- If after a few days your baby is still not directly breastfeeding, a nipple shield, which is made of thin flexible silicone, may help them transition back to the breast.[23]

- You could try a feeding tube, which is taped to your clean finger so that the baby receives the breast milk whilst they are sucking on your finger.[24]

- A breast milk supplementer is a device that allows the baby to receive milk at the breast via a fine tube that is carrying milk from a container (often worn on a cord around the mum's neck) to the nipple.[25]

If you are considering using any of the above techniques or devices, please seek skilled help from a breastfeeding specialist or lactation consultant.[26]

---

[22] Visit Association of Breastfeeding Mothers for more advice https://abm.me.uk/breastfeeding-information/relactation/.
[23] Visit La Leche for further information https://www.laleche.org.uk/nipple-shields/.
[24] Learn more about finger feeding at https://breastfeeding.support/what-is-finger-feeding/.
[25] Read more at https://www.laleche.org.uk/nursing-supplementers/.
[26] You can gain further advice and support from the NHS https://www.nhs.uk/conditions/baby/breastfeeding-and-bottle-

Where to find help

While we've included lots of resources in this section to support you, there is of course an abundance of specialist help available to you, both in hospital and as home visits.

There are many members of the multi-disciplinary team who can support you and work with the doctors, nurses and midwives who are taking care of you both.

Ask the staff to put you in touch with the NHS Infant Specialist Team/Lead available at the trust. You may even find them listed on the hospital or trust website. All Maternity and Neonatal Units should have a designated lead who are working towards the current standards of UNICEF and Baby Friendly Accreditation.[27] Together they will help support you with feeding and establishing a strong relationship.

Specialist Paediatric Dieticians help babies and children with eating and drinking challenges, and have in depth specialist knowledge of the properties and components of breast and formula milk.[28]

Speech and Language Therapists (SALT) provide support with babies and children who are experiencing challenges with feeding and swallowing.[29]

First Steps Nutrition Trust is an independent public health nutrition charity that provides information free from conflict of interest on all modes of feeding and milk.[30]

It's also worth mentioning that some hospitals provide breastfeeding mums with free food vouchers, if their baby is a patient in the hospital. Speak with your hospital to check if they provide these, which you can then use at the hospital canteen.

feeding/breastfeeding/help-and-support/ and from the Lactation Consultants of Great Britain https://lcgb.org.
[27] Visit www.unicef.org.uk/babyfriendly for more information.
[28] Visit www.bda.uk.com.
[29] Visit www.reslt.org for further support.
[30] For more detail visit www.firststeps.nutrition.org.

CHAPTER 6
Cleaning; for all children who require clean environments

Cleaning for me became a coping mechanism – a way in which I felt I could help Bailey and keep him free from possible infections.

When it comes to cleaning when you have a child with CF, things aren't just clean, they are "CF clean". It's a whole new level of cleaning.

When I entered the world of cystic fibrosis, I wanted a clear and concise list given to me about what needed cleaning, throwing or changing in our house so I could give Bailey the best possible chance. One didn't exist. So I've composed one here as best and extensively as I can.

These might predominantly be relevant to those living with CF, focusing heavily on areas of potential bacteria through stagnant water, but some might also be helpful hygiene points for anyone with weak immune systems or recovering from hospital treatments.

Some people may feel this is too much, or equally not enough, but I believe it's about doing what feels right for you and your family, so take from this what you will and feel free to ignore the rest, or do more. (And yes, you'll wish you had shares in Dettol.)

Sinks
An absolute breeding ground for germs, and little pools of water. I took to scrubbing mine thoroughly with Dettol and dousing with bleach regularly.

Cutlery drainers
Ensure you have one that allows the water to drain through otherwise stagnant water will gather at the bottom.

Dishcloths
Sponges, J cloths, scourers; they are all another growth point for bacteria, so I change ours every few days to avoid any potential build-up of bacteria.

Tea towels
These can again be a source of bad bacteria, so these are now changed every couple of days, and are hung to dry between uses.

Toothbrush holder
Most toothbrush holders are enclosed, so they gather water droplets when you leave your wet toothbrush to stand. I found a metal one that offers free drainage so there is no collection point. Visit www.laura-barrett.co.uk to download our Best Buys, including this toothbrush holder.

Bath toys
Many have holes in the bottom that collect water, where it stays and becomes stagnant, such as a hole in the bottom of a rubber duck. Some parents choose not to have water toys at all, however we chose a couple of beakers, a rubber duck without a hole in the bottom and a couple of the plastic flip-over floaters. The latter are great as they can blow on them to flip them over to reveal another colour, also working their lungs for some extra physiotherapy (discover at www.laura-barrett.co.uk). We wash these out with Dettol and boiling water every so often.

Showers
Mildew and mould can build up in the seals so clean and Dettol regularly.

Plug holes
Literally throw a glug of bleach down them every day or so as there's no knowing what lurks in a plug hole.

Door handles
Think how many times handles are touched and how often they actually get cleaned? With guests aplenty and other children in the house, I used to clean our door handles weekly with disinfectant, but it's more like fortnightly now.

Common touch points
These include front door handles (inside and outside), remote controls, mobile phones, keys and taps. I disinfect all regularly, compared to never, before we all lived with CF.

Shoes
We are a no-shoes household. Non-negotiable. End of.

Dust

Sweep, dust and vacuum often to avoid a build-up of dust, because these small particles could aggravate breathing issues.

Floors

A mop and bucket of water doesn't cut it. The water gets dirty and in my mind I'm simply spreading that dirt around the house. Floor steam cleaners are the way forward, killing around 99% of all germs, with a pad that I can change and throw in the washing machine for next time. Far more hygienic, CF or not. Another option are the disposable floor wipes that attach to the mop.

To discover our favourite steam cleaner, with attachments for floors, walls and a versatile nozzle that we use anywhere, including the toilet, visit www.laura-barrett.co.uk.

UV steriliser

These sterilisers can be used for baby bottles, but also for everyday items such as keys, for example. They use UV rays, rather than water, and eliminate 99.9% of germs.

Flowers

Water in vases becomes stagnant after a few days. I'm sure there are plenty of people who still have real flowers, but I prefer to avoid them completely and instead now adorn my home with the most beautiful, life-like artificial stems. They're less upkeep, don't wilt and I don't have to stress about refreshing the water every day or so to avoid stagnant germs.

Water bottles

Most offer practical non-drip nozzles, but these are a known collection point for water and even mildew if not cleaned properly. I did use these short term, but removed the inside rubber part every day and washed under very hot water and let air dry. I quickly moved on to an opened nozzle bottle that's easy to clean and doesn't allow any water to get stuck. Discover our top ones at www.laura-barrett.co.uk.

Straws
I avoid a straw-style nozzle on a re-useable water bottle, as well as metal re-useable straws. Recyclable paper straws could be an alternative.

Outside the home

Paddling pool
I do still let the boys have a paddling pool even though it makes me feel uneasy, but I change the water every day. Every time I put it away, I allow it to air dry thoroughly, then I Dettol it down, and Dettol it again when I get it back out.

Balls
Once a ball has been used outside and is covered in mud, we wipe them down with Dettol. We also have outdoor-specific balls and those just for indoors.

Water play stations, sand pits, mud and mud kitchens
These all fall under the same category really, and whether you let your child play with these so they don't feel different is totally each parent's choice. Either way, a thorough hand wash with anti-bacterial soap is highly recommended.

Water butts, ponds and fish tanks
All rife with stagnant water so there's a common tendency to avoid these due to the bacteria that can build up. We removed our garden water butts and don't have any ponds or fish tanks.

Swings
Again I often wiped down the swing before using, especially the front bar and side rails where children hold.

Trolley seats and handles
Grab yourself a Dettol wipe from your handbag and give it a clean before putting baby in the seat.

For all our suggested best buys, visit www.laura-barrett.co.uk **to access the free download.**

CHAPTER 7
Cystic fibrosis facts and questions, answered

Through this book, and specifically this chapter, I hope to raise awareness of the little-known condition of cystic fibrosis, as well as provide accurate and available information to those who have received a recent diagnosis and are new to the CF community.

Through facts and knowledge, the hope is that people will know more about cystic fibrosis, whether it's in their family genetics and have a better understanding should they know someone with CF. Knowledge is power. Open and honest is the best way forward, no matter how hard some of the truth is.

❖ Cystic fibrosis is a genetic condition that affects just over 10,800 people in the UK.

❖ One in 25 of us carry the faulty CF gene, but most of us don't know it.

❖ CF is a recessive genetic condition, meaning you need to pick up faulty genes from both parents to have CF.

❖ The odds of two people who carry the gene having a baby with cystic fibrosis is 1 in 4 (25%).

❖ They test for CF during the newborn screening heel prick test in the UK, usually five days after birth.

❖ Five babies are born with CF each week in the UK.

❖ The gene affected by CF controls the movement of salt and water in and out of cells.

❖ Cystic fibrosis is often thought of as a lung condition, due to respiratory issues, but it affects many parts of the body, including the digestive system, liver and more.

❖ People with CF experience a build-up of thick, sticky mucus in their lungs, digestive system and other organs.

❖ It's difficult to expel the bacteria from their lungs due to thick mucus, which in turn can cause frequent infections and subsequent lung damage.

❖ Many people living with CF are pancreas insufficient, so have to take Creon Micro enzymes when they eat to absorb fat and protein. Even then, due to malabsorption, those with CF require 20%-50% more calories each day than those without CF.

❖ Those living with CF lose salt, so require a high-salt diet to replenish their losses, plus their skin and tears taste saltier too. A sweat test is one of the ways to diagnose cystic fibrosis, as well as blood tests.

❖ Some people develop CF-related liver disease and CF-related diabetes.

❖ There are more than 1,400 different mutations of the faulty cystic fibrosis gene, called a genotype, with Delta F508 being the most common.

❖ A person's CF genotype doesn't indicate the severity of their condition; it simply varies from person to person so everybody's journey is unique to them.

❖ People with CF cannot meet due to the risk of passing harmful bacteria and infections between each other.

❖ Daily physiotherapy is required, often including a PEP (Positive Expiratory Pressure) mask, breathing techniques and bouncing to help loosen the mucus in the lungs.

❖ Cough swabs are taken regularly to check for potential infections. This allows them to identify the bacteria growing and give a targeted antibiotic. This might be an oral antibiotic administered from home, or an IV antibiotic from hospital or home.

❖ Most men with cystic fibrosis (98%) will be infertile. The sperm is healthy, but it is unable to travel to the egg, so they will usually require IVF support to have children.

❖ One of the very best treatments for CF is exercise.

❖ Average life expectancy for those living with cystic fibrosis is currently about 50 years old, according to the 2020 UK CF Registry.

❖ Two young lives are lost to CF every week.

❖ There is currently no cure for CF.[31]

---

[31] All information taken from the CF Trust website https://www.cysticfibrosis.org.uk and GOSH NHS UK website https://www.gosh.nhs.uk/conditions-and-treatments/conditions-we-treat/cystic-fibrosis-0/, correct as of March 2022.

Symptoms of cystic fibrosis

Cystic fibrosis is tested for on the day five newborn heel prick blood test taken in the UK. However, sometimes symptoms of CF can be evident before that time, including:

- Unable to gain weight, despite drinking lots of milk (called 'failure to thrive').
- Constantly hungry despite feeding frequently.
- Unable to pass minimal/any meconium (known as meconium ileus).
- Green-tinged sick.
- Distended/swollen tummy.
- Salty taste to their skin when kissed.

Of course, many of these can be indicators of other things, some merely constipation, but they are some signs that could potentially relate to cystic fibrosis.

Cystic fibrosis questions, answered

The reason I want to answer all of my own questions from the moment Bailey was diagnosed, is because if we had all those questions whirring around our heads, surely other new parents of a baby with CF also have similar questions?

I know some of the questions listed are silly, but you don't know what you don't know, until someone tells you. And sometimes people might feel too self-conscious to ask certain things, or might turn to sources that accidentally misinform.

This chapter is so important to me, as I would have loved to have had access to some of this information all in one place that I could read over as and when I needed. I hope it is all you need too, as and when you are ready to read it.

The more factual answers have been taken from the CF Trust website or obtained via conversations with Bailey's care team to ensure accurate information and advice. Some answers have an element of personal choice, in which case take what you need and ignore what you don't. The overriding message with CF is to do what feels right for you and your child, and seek advice from your CF care team directly should you need.

My questions were a stream of consciousness that I noted down in my journal and asked at our CF Education Day, but here I've categorised them into the following sections to create an easier reference guide for you to use. I've also merged a few of the questions together as they ultimately have the same answer. Note that all questions are written from me, hence 'he' refers to Bailey.

1. Genetics, diagnosis and life expectancy
2. Water, mud, sand and smoke
3. Treatments; current and future
4. Lungs, and other organs
5. Practical, everyday questions
6. Emotional thoughts and worries

1. Genetics, diagnosis and life expectancy

What CF genes does he have?

There are around 1,400 cystic fibrosis mutations, with the most common being Delta F508. Each child is given their genetic mutation or genotype on diagnosis.

From his gene type, can you tell if it is a severe case? Are there any signs he has a bad case?

In short, the answer is no, but I know that's not the answer you want to hear.

I begged Bailey's CF care team to tell me what his genes meant for his health and future, and I asked daily if they saw any indicators of what awaited him. My pleas remain unanswered.

Two people with exactly the same mutations could have very different journeys with CF.

You could have two siblings with the same genotype, and one is constantly in hospital and dies far too young, while the other lives a long and active life. There is no rhyme or reason to it – it's just the unknown nature of CF.

Take the founder of Trunki as an example. Rob Law and his twin sister Kate were both born with CF. Rob is now the owner of this successful global ride-on luggage company and a father to three children. His sister Kate had a heart and lung transplant aged 15 and sadly died four months later.[32]

As twins, they had the same genetic mutation and the same upbringing. What was the cause of their very different lives with cystic fibrosis?

Are his gene types easy or less easy to treat? Is the gene from Kev any better/worse than the gene from me?

They told me it made no difference, but now that I know so much more about CF, my honest answer would be that the gene Bailey inherited from Kev is better.

Kev's CF gene is the Delta F508, which is the most common CF gene, so research and treatments are heavily focused around it. Less treatments are available to those without Delta F508, who instead perhaps have more unique genes. Around 90% of those living with CF have the Delta F508 gene.

In terms of the impact the genes have on the person's health, then no, it isn't the defining factor on how well or not a child fares in life. There simply doesn't seem to be any defining factor about what causes a more or less severe case of CF, as mentioned above, which is a really hard fact to accept. Lifestyle and commitment to medicine and physiotherapy of course play a significant role, but seemingly not the gene type directly.

Is this lack of knowledge common for parents of CF children?

Sadly, yes. Around one in twenty-five people unknowingly carry the CF gene. So many parents are completely unaware of what cystic fibrosis is, let alone the fact they themselves harbour one faulty CF gene. When their child is then diagnosed with the condition, shock and disbelief set in.

This is because CF is a recessive genetic condition, so parents can carry one CF gene with absolutely no symptoms. It is only when their child inherits *both* the mum's and dad's CF genes, that they are born with CF and the whole genetic heritage becomes known.

Was there any way I could have known I/we carried the CF gene?

If there is anyone is your family with CF, then there is a chance you too could carry the gene. Speaking openly and honestly about CF is very

---

[32] *65 Roses and a Trunki; Defying the Odds in Life and Business,* written by Rob Law.

important so that everyone in the family is aware of it and what they need to do.

Now you are here, and you know that CF is in both your families' genetics, it is imperative that you encourage other family members to be tested to check if they too carry the CF gene, particularly those who might soon start a family of their own. This could include siblings, cousins, aunts, uncles – anyone who sits in your family tree, including any other children of your own.

Anyone in your family could be a carrier of the same gene as you, and having the knowledge of their genetic makeup will help them going forward. Your hospital can provide a letter of your child's CF diagnosis, which your family members can share with their GP to request the genetic blood test.

If he has a child one day, and his partner is not a carrier of the CF gene, can he produce a CF child as he has two copies of the CF gene?

No, because only one of their faulty CF genes will be inherited, while the other gene comes from the other biological parent.

Providing the other parent isn't a carrier of the gene, then the child will not be born with CF. If the other biological parent is a carrier of the gene, then there is a two in four (50%) chance of having a child with cystic fibrosis.

However, the child will definitely be a carrier of the CF gene as the baby will inherit at least one CF gene from the parent who has CF.

What is the life expectancy of someone with CF? Is it true the life expectancy is 47?

As with everything with cystic fibrosis, it varies from one person to the next. According to the CF Trust, half of people born in 2017 would live to 47 years old. The most recent stat from the 2020 UK CF Registry has actually increased to 50 years. Despite these averages, of course some might live to be older, while others sadly die much younger. The median age of those with CF who died in 2020 was 36 years old.

I'm sorry. I know it isn't long enough and I know how much it hurts. I can't imagine what it must be like for people living with an age above their head; wondering each day if they are going to live to their target age, out-live it or fall short.

None of us know what the future holds for our children, and nobody can predict the age at which they pass, but there is something about knowing there is a set limit to their life.

Yet it's crucial to take comfort believing that thanks to amazing drugs coming through for cystic fibrosis, it is highly likely babies diagnosed with CF today might far exceed this number.

There's a saying I once read, 'Give yourself a life expectancy. That will force you to live'. If there's one positive thing I can say to you at this stage, it's that this is true. It will be true for both your child, and for you as parents.

Once you find your feet, there will be a renewed vigour to live life, to not waste a moment and to do the things you once took for granted.

Do we still lose very young children from CF?

Sadly, the answer is yes, but thankfully not nearly as young nor as often these days. Back in the Sixties, children would be lucky to live past the age of five years old and parents were often told not to register their child for school, fearing they might not live that long.

Nowadays, due to the most amazing medical advancements, our CF population has access to enzymes that help them absorb food and thrive, medicines that specifically target different infections and constant reviews so anything can be picked up early and treated accordingly. If ever you had to live with cystic fibrosis, now is the time. There is more hope today than there has ever been.

Are there benefits to being diagnosed so young?

Yes, lots. The younger a child is diagnosed with CF the sooner they can get the treatment they require to thrive. They can access Creon[33] to help them absorb food and therefore grow healthily, they can start physio to help keep well and they will have a dedicated care team to assess and treat potential infections.

Left undiagnosed, a child might struggle to gain weight, be unwell regularly, suffer infections they can't clear because they don't have access to required antibiotics and be exposed to lifestyle factors that could worsen their condition.

---

[33] See section 3 in this chapter for information on Creon.

It is for these reasons that since 2007, the UK routinely test for cystic fibrosis via the heel prick test on day five of newborn screenings. According to data from the 2020 UK CF Registry, the median age for diagnosis is 22 days old.

Have my older boys got CF?

Although it was unlikely, when I asked it could not be answered without a sweat test. The sweat test showed that our older boys do not have cystic fibrosis, but they could still be carriers of one CF gene. We won't be able to test for this until they are 18, because in the UK the parents cannot decide on this test on behalf of the child. They must choose for themselves to have the test once they're adults.

All full biological siblings of those living with CF could either carry the CF gene or have CF, because they were created from the same parenting gene pool. If you wish to get any of your other children tested, you can speak to your CF care team.

Will you sweat test them for me?

Great Ormond Street Hospital kindly carried out the sweat test on Harry and Mylo for us to give us absolute certainty they didn't have CF.

People with CF lose a lot of salt, which increases the amount of chloride (as salt) in their sweat, compared with those who do not have the condition. The sweat test is used to detect abnormally high levels of chloride and help establish, or exclude, a diagnosis of cystic fibrosis.

A small watch-like band is put around the wrist, which is stimulated by a current from a battery, for around five minutes. This doesn't hurt, but might give a tingling sensation and leave the skin a little red. The sweat is collected into the coil for several minutes, before being taken to the laboratory for analysis.

I was scanned at 20 and 38 weeks' gestation. Why was the meconium ileus not picked up on the scan?[34] Was my reduced fetal movement linked to all of this?

This question still doesn't sit right with me. I actually hate even thinking about it. It's so odd to think that people were examining my unborn child and

---

[34] Refer to section 4 of this chapter for information on meconium ileus.

didn't 'see' anything. But was there anything to visibly see and why would they even be looking for this when there was no known reason to do so?

Some cases of sonographic diagnosis of meconium ileus in utero are possible, based on masses in the ileum and dilated bowel.[35]

There is a chance that Bailey's reduced fetal movements were related to his CF and meconium ileus, but we will never know. It might have been that I simply wasn't resting enough between running around after two young, active boys.

In reality, this is one of those questions I've had to let go, just like the following one. I hope you can, too.

Why do we test for CF on day five newborn heel prick and not in utero?

Answering this question would open a political and never-ending debate, which won't serve anyone, nor end well.

I mulled over this for months, leading into years. I couldn't get away from it. We check for so much in utero, so why not CF?

The way I settled the argument in my head was to ask myself this powerful question: 'If I knew while pregnant, what difference would it make and what would I have done with the knowledge?'

Looking at Bailey and all the joy he has given us, I was able to let go of this thought and free myself from its pain. I truly hope you're able to as well.

---

[35] Parikh NS, Ibrahim S, Ahlawat R, 'Meconium Ileus', *StatPearls*, updated August 2021 and Goldstein RB, Filly RA, Callen PW, 'Sonographic diagnosis of meconium ileus in utero', *Journal of Ultrasound in Medicine*, 1987 Nov;6(11):663-6.

2. Water, mud, sand and smoke

I asked about these, because I was made increasingly aware of some key areas that could harbour bacteria, which could prove detrimental to Bailey's health.

Are bacteria in stagnant water airborne or just from touch?

Water is the natural environment for Pseudomonas aeruginosa – harmful bacteria for those living with cystic fibrosis. Once it takes hold, it's tricky to eradicate, and many people living with CF have to simply manage this chronic infection with daily nebulised antibiotics.

Pseudomonas can be transmitted by direct contact, such as kissing, or indirect contact by touching door knobs, toys, remotes, phones and other objects that have been previously touched by someone carrying the organism.

It can also be airborne by coughing and sneezing (referred to as, "aerosol") as it's believed that droplets can remain in a room long enough to put those with CF at risk.[36]

Are tea towels a source of bad bacteria? Sinks? Toilet brush holders? Sponges?

Yes, yes, yes and yes. All of these harbour bacteria that could potentially cause infection in those living with CF.

The simplest way I think of it, is that absolutely anything retaining stagnant water is a red zone. We change our tea towels and hand towels every couple of days and leave them hung to dry between uses. We don't use sponges at all. Sinks, toilets and toilet brush holders are cleaned regularly with germ-killing bleach and Dettol. (For more information on cleaning, see chapter 6.)

How frequently you clean and change everything just depends how heightened you want to be to the situation. Some people will change them all the time and still get infections, while others won't be overly cautious and might not be impacted too greatly.

Everyone's cystic fibrosis journey is so different and the way people choose to live their life around it is so personal.

---

[36] Clifton IJ, Peckham DG. 'Defining routes of airborne transmission of Pseudomonas aeruginosa in people with cystic fibrosis', *Expert Review of Respiratory Medicine*, volume 4, issue 4, August 2010.

Bath toys?

Ones with holes in them, such as plastic ducks with a hole in the bottom or things that can shoot out water, aren't ideal as they can't be fully emptied and dried out. The water gets trapped inside, becomes stagnant and could grow bacteria.

Discover some suitable bath toys on our Best Buys download at www.laura-barrett.co.uk.

Are stagnant toothbrushes bad for Bailey?

Much research has gone into this area. Toothbrushes are of course an everyday essential, but their damp, stagnant nature could be a breeding ground for bacteria.

Research shows that certain bacteria could grow on used toothbrushes, and could potentially transmit microorganisms from the environment to the mouth and eventually to the lower airways.[37]

Advice is to change the toothbrush every three months as usual, and to use a new toothbrush following an infection. Some advice also recommends to steam clean the toothbrush after every use or every day, which was shown to eradicate potential organisms.[38]

Can he attend swimming lessons?

Yes, little ones with CF can go swimming and attend lessons. In fact, swimming is actually a great form of exercise for those living with cystic fibrosis.

Nuffield Health offer a CF Programme, giving free access to their gyms and health clubs, plus one-to-one personal training once they're old enough. They are partnered with many trusts and CF care teams across the UK, so it's worth checking for more information.

We've enjoyed many swimming sessions at our local Nuffield – it's so clean and quiet, minimising the risk of possible infections.

---

[37] Passarelli Mantovani, Rebeca et al. 'Toothbrushes may convey bacteria to the cystic fibrosis lower airways', *Journal of Oral Microbiology* vol. 11,1 1647036. 7 August 2019.
[38] Beverley C Miller, Mollie Maguire et al. 'Steam disinfection of toothbrushes from patients with cystic fibrosis: Evidence-based recommendations', *Paediatric Pulmonology,* volume 55, issue 11, 30 July 2020.

Are paddling pools OK?

These need to be cleaned and dried thoroughly between uses, and have the water refreshed daily when being enjoyed. (Refer to chapter 6 for further information on cleaning paddling pools.)

Saunas? Steam rooms? Jacuzzis?

These are to be avoided.

Warm water that is aerolised (converted into a fine spray or mist) can be inhaled directly into the lungs. If the water contains Pseudomonas, it could lead to infections in those living with CF. The water, warmth, aeration and human contamination prevent adequate disinfection and provide an ideal environment for the growth of Pseudomonas.[39]

The same applies to greenhouses and butterfly houses where they often use misting systems.

Aerolised water is even something to consider within the home. Shower heads can sometimes contain Pseudomonas, and when the shower starts running, aerolised droplets could potentially be inhaled. It's therefore recommended to let the shower run for 1-2 minutes before the person with CF steps in.[40]

Elsewhere in the bathroom, it is also suggested that toilet lids are closed down before flushing to avoid any potential spray or droplets. Toilets can contain many bacteria, so regularly cleaning with bleach and Dettol is a very good idea.

Can he swim in the sea?

Yes, those living with CF can swim in the sea.

Thoughts are that the cold temperature and free flowing tides will prevent the growth of Pseudomonas. Plus, the high salt content present in sea water also helps inhibit the growth of this bacteria.[41]

However, of course there is a risk of human faeces being present in water near the shoreline. Again, perhaps this is a personal choice, and it might be

---

[39] *Govan & Nelson, 1993 [III]; Govan, 2000 [IV].*
[40] NHS Royal Brompton and Harefield Hospitals, *Appendix 3 – Risks of getting P. aeruginosa from the environment, Caring for Children with cystic fibrosis.*
[41] Cystic Fibrosis Trust study, *Pseudomonas aeruginosa infection in people with cystic fibrosis. Suggestions for Prevention and Infection Control,* Second Edition November 2004, section 2.1.

worth checking the quality of the water where you are swimming before making a decision. In the UK, you can do this on the Government website.[42]

Would it be beneficial to live by the sea?
The sea air itself has also been shown to have beneficial affects to those with CF.

Years ago, doctors in Australia noticed that surfers with CF had healthier lungs. They determined that inhaling the saltwater mist has positive effects on rehydrating the lining of the lungs and helps eliminate bacteria-contaminated mucus. This discovery lead to the development of a hypertonic saline solution that many people with CF around the world inhale daily.[43]

Will the sea air cure your child? No. Could the sea air help alleviate possible lung infections and potentially help airway clearance? Maybe.

There's been many an occasion where I've wondered about moving from our rural, wet and muddy countryside home to the coast for a daily dose of fresh, crisp sea air. I allow Bailey to swim in the sea and enjoy our days by the beach where I truly believe it is doing him the world of good.

Is a drier climate, such as Spain, a better place to live?
Of course, drier climates have less dampness and less of the cold winter bug spread every parent, but especially parents of CF children, dread.

However, what I realised is that you cannot run from CF. It will always find you. Wherever you live, these environmental bacteria exist. What matters the most is that you are around those that love and support you in this journey, and that you do all you can to give your little one the happiest, healthiest start in life – which you absolutely will.

Sandpits?
Often these might be dry on top, but damp underneath, so could be harbouring harmful bacteria, such as Pseudomonas. It's recommended that outdoor sandpits always have a lid on to keep dry when it rains and the advice

---

[42] Visit https://www.gov.uk/quality-of-local-bathing-water.
[43] Rosenfeld, M., Davis, S., Brumback, L., Daniel, S., Rowbotham, R., Johnson, R., McNamara, S., Jensen, R., Barlow, C. and Ratjen, F. (2011), *Inhaled hypertonic saline in infants and toddlers with cystic fibrosis: short-term tolerability, adherence, and safety.* Published in Pediatric Pulmonology, 46: 666-671.

is that they are cleaned with steriliser once a week, whether that's at home, nursery or schools. Obviously public park ones won't have been cleaned.

I personally avoid them altogether and Bailey is given his own little tray of fresh sand to play with, which is kept indoors.

Mud?

Again, caution needs to be taken around mud due to the potential presence of Pseudomonas.[44] However, that said, mud is not aerolised like water, so it's only if the mud goes in their mouth or nose that it's a potential source of infection.[45]

Playing in the garden should definitely be allowed. A thorough hand wash, including under nails, is highly recommended though after playing, and try to get children to not put soiled hands in their noses and mouths (I know, I said *try*).

Muddy kitchens are common play area in gardens, nurseries and some schools. Whether you feel comfortable with your child playing with them or not is totally your decision.

Soil with added fertiliser or manure is best avoided.

If mud is bad for him, how can he possibly play rugby and football?

In truth, there is a risk of potential infection, but then there is with everything in life. It's about getting the balance between having quality of life, while still being cautious. Plus, given exercise is so beneficial, this one is the balance between the benefits and the risks.

An exceptional good hand wash immediately after playing and a hefty dose of antibacterial hand gel are essential for any sideline mum. Our family also has designated indoor and outdoor balls, and we Dettol dirty outdoor balls frequently.

With team sports, it's also advised to avoid sharing water bottles with the team on the pitch (and in any situation), and some people choose to avoid the friendly handshake with the opposition and instead opt for a fist pump.

---

[44] Cystic Fibrosis Trust study, 'Pseudomonas aeruginosa infection in people with cystic fibrosis. Suggestions for Prevention and Infection Control', Second Edition, November 2004, section 2.1.
[45] NHS Royal Brompton and Harefield Hospitals, *Appendix 3 – Risks of getting P. aeruginosa from the environment, Caring for Children with cystic fibrosis.*

What do I do if friends have fish tanks/fish ponds?

These should be avoided due to the stagnant water and potential bacteria, especially warm water tanks for tropical fish.

If you're visiting a friend with one, simply keep your distance from it and avoid touching it. If you do, wash hands well afterwards.

Stagnant ponds and canals should also be avoided, as should water butts. Compost heaps and bags of decaying vegetation should also be avoided.[46]

Can he paddle in our village stream?

Yes, but again it's personal choice and another thorough hand wash and anti-bacterial gel would be recommended. A clear, free flowing stream is obviously a slightly better option than a very stagnant, dirty spot.

The same could be said for lakes, with very stagnant lakes best avoided. This said, some people with CF who I follow on social media regularly swim in lakes without hesitation and experiences no ill effects, so again, it's personal choice.

Can I still have real flowers or is water in a vase bad for him?

Yes, you can still have real flowers, but its recommended to change the water every day to ensure its fresh and free from potential bacteria.

I choose to no longer have real flowers as I don't feel comfortable with it, and love my artificial blooms, but it's personal choice.

If my boys pick me wild flowers, am I allowed to keep them?

Yes, but you would ideally refresh the water each day.

Should we now have a fake Christmas tree?

You don't have to, no, however we do now have an artificial tree, which actually worked out to be a great decision both in terms of cost and convenience. It's simply one less thing to worry about in terms of stagnant water in the stand.

---

[46] NHS Royal Brompton and Harefield Hospitals, *Appendix 3 – Risks of getting P. aeruginosa from the environment, Caring for Children with cystic fibrosis.*

Can he be around smoky environments?

Smoking and second-hand smoke is not good for anyone, and certainly not for those living with CF.

Breathing in smoke can damage the cilia lining the airways, causing mucus to become trapped. Given inflammation and mucus build-up are already problems within someone with CF, this exacerbates the issues further. Regular exposure to smoke could cause respiratory damage, increased lung infections, reduced lung function and increased inflammation in those with CF.[47]

Second-hand smoke is even more detrimental to children with CF as they breathe faster than adults, resulting in more chemicals, irritants and carcinogens entering their lungs.

It's therefore important to keep your child in smoke-free environments. Don't allow someone to smoke near your child, or move seats if you feel the smoke is still blowing over you, even outside.

Don't go in a car in which someone is smoking or has been smoking, and ideally not in a smoker's home either. Third-hand smoke lingers in carpets, clothes and furniture, so if you have family that smoke, you might want to ask them to change into fresh clothes if they're going to hold your baby, and maybe suggest meeting somewhere outside of their home if they smoke indoors. If you smoke, it's advised to find support to quit.

Is it OK to be near a fire/fire pit/bonfire?

There doesn't appear to be a simple yes or no answer to this. Naturally, any fire place should be well flued, and if near a fire pit or bonfire, it is suggested not to stand down wind to avoid being in the smoke.

Some people with cystic fibrosis claim they can't be near anything like this, while others enjoy a fire at home on a regular basis. It doesn't seem to be a one rule fits all, like many things with CF.

---

[47] Benjamin T Kopp et al, 'The Impact of Secondhand Smoke Exposure on Children with Cystic Fibrosis: A Review', *International Journal of Environmental Research and Public Health*, October 2016.

Can I burn candles at home?

Our care team said that we could, yes. Some research suggests that a natural soy wax would be a better option.

On reading, some people living with cystic fibrosis do report that they can feel it in their lungs when they burn candles, while it doesn't affect others, so again everyone is different.

3. Treatments; current and future

Will he have lots of hospital appointments?
This varies from one person to the next. Some people with CF go months or years without being admitted to hospital, while others are regulars on the ward.

However, most people with cystic fibrosis will be under a care team that sees them every two to three months for regular checks, plus an annual assessment. If they have other CF-related issues, such as liver disease, then they will also have appointments with specialists for that, sometimes at a different hospital.

You mentioned physiotherapy equipment – what are they referring to exactly?
Physiotherapy equipment changes as your child grows up, but they are all focused on airway clearance to help stop thick mucus building up and blocking the airways in the lungs, reducing infections and preventing lung damage.

Physio varies from one individual to the next, but they usually include Positive Expiratory Pressure (PEP), which can be a mask, mouthpiece or simply blowing bubbles. A range of breathing techniques are used, as well as percussion, vibration and bouncing.

In short, anything to work the lungs and help loosen the thick mucus. Your physio team will work closely with your child and their activities will change over the years based on their age and health.

Then of course there's exercise, something that truly must be encouraged in those living with CF.

You can also find some other fun physio ideas on our free download at www.laura-barrett.co.uk.

What is Creon and are there long-term effects of taking it?
Many people with CF are pancreas insufficient and require enzyme support via Creon.

Ordinarily, the pancreas creates enzymes which break down fat, protein and carbohydrates to digest food and release nutrients so the body can make energy.

In those with CF, the small tubes that transport these enzymes out of the pancreas become blocked with mucus, causing the enzymes to build up in the pancreas rather than reach the digestive system.

Creon is made from the pancreas of pigs, the same pigs people eat for pork, and contains a mix of all the pancreatic enzymes – lipase, amylase and protease. People with CF take Creon before eating foods with fat and protein so their body can digest and absorb the food, and babies take it before their milk.

There are other enzyme brands available, but before the late 1980s these little miracle workers didn't exist at all, leaving many people living with CF malnourished and underweight, only exacerbating their poor health.

Although Creon works wonders in absorption for those with CF, there is still some malabsorption, so a high-fat diet is still required to make up for losses to ensure sufficient weight gain.

According to the Creon website, common side effects of long-term use of Creon include increased or decreased blood sugars, abdominal pain, abnormal bowel movements, gas, vomiting, dizziness, sore throat and an increased risk of a rare bowel disorder called fibrosing colonopathy.[48] We personally haven't seen any of these side effects in Bailey so far.

Does he have to have Creon with snacks?

It depends what the snack is. Any foods and drinks containing fat and protein require Creon. How much Creon depends on the fat or protein quantity, and also varies from child to child depending on their Creon demands.

Any foods without fat and protein, such as vegetables, fruit and ice lollies, will not require Creon.

Do I always have to give Creon on apple puree or is pear puree OK?

Either is fine, but ideally it's good to be consistent to forge strong and familiar habits for your baby. Obviously if you run out of fruit puree of any description, administering it with anything is better than not at all. We got caught short once and just used a little yoghurt.

---

[48] https://www.creon.co.uk/-/media/creoncouk/assets/pdf/uk_pi_creon_021_final.pdf?la=en-gb

If he takes ages eating his food, but Creon was given at the beginning, then how do I manage that? Does he require more Creon?
We tend to give one scoop/capsule at the start of the meal, and then while he is eating we give a little more if we think he needs it based on how much he has eaten. We then give a bit more once he starts his dessert, if it's yoghurt for example, so we're topping up the Creon as we go.

If I am breastfeeding, I don't know how much milk he is having, so how do I calculate how much Creon to give?
This is a bit of guess work, it's true, but with all babies with CF, the best indicator is their stool frequency and consistency.

If your milk-fed baby is producing copious amounts of dirty nappies, and/or the poo has a slight fatty shine to it showing malabsorption, then you'll want to chat to your CF care team about potentially needing to increase their Creon dose.

This is a moving target though, because of course their feeds are always increasing as they grow, so it's a continual work in progress. I found Bailey's Creon and absorption balance to be at its best once he was fully weaned onto solids.

Are there long-term effects of taking Flucloxacillin?
Flucloxacillin is an antibiotic that most babies with CF take daily as a preventative to getting infections, rather than a treatment for when they have an infection.

Taking antibiotics kills both good and bad bacteria in the gut, plus some antibiotics can cause an upset tummy and also increase sensitivity to the sun, among other potential side effects. Specifically, Flucloxacillin is known to potentially cause liver issues with prolonged use.

Research is still ongoing via the CF Start study to help decipher if babies with CF who take this antibiotic experience better health and less infections, compared with those children who do not take it.

Bailey was on the CF Start study, taking Flucloxacillin daily. However, he developed liver issues at two years old, and although we don't know if this contributed to it, we stopped his daily dose of this antibiotic to see if it helped the issue.

Should he take a probiotic to help his gut?
The CF dietician has never outwardly said this, however we felt that we wanted to support Bailey's gut health with a daily probiotic, due to the amount of antibiotics he takes.

We educated ourselves on the power of the gut and how so much of our health and wellbeing, inside and out, stems from the microbiome, so it made sense for us to support the very thing that could help keep Bailey well.

We did show the CF dietician the probiotic we were giving Bailey just to get her opinion and also let her know what he was taking. It's always good to be transparent with your CF care team so they have the whole picture of your child's wellbeing and lifestyle.

Is gene therapy a possibility?
The cystic fibrosis genetic mutations mean that the cells have an error in their instructions (in this case, the CFTR gene), so the protein is not made properly, or is not sent to the cell surface where it is needed. Genetic medicines could correct the mistake in the gene so that they function properly.

Gene therapy involves inserting an extra copy of a healthy gene into a cell to replace the faulty one. Whereas gene editing fixes the error in the gene in the cell.

Gene therapy and gene editing are areas that are being heavily researched by the CF Trust in the UK.

The CF Trust is funding a world-class Strategic Research Centre exploring gene editing to create a new treatment that will fix the mutation that causes the build-up of mucus in the lungs. They also funded the UK Gene Therapy Consortium (GTC) to develop a gene therapy product with the potential to correct the faulty cystic fibrosis gene in the lungs.

There is so much to discover in this area, and it could be hugely positive for the CF community.

Does cannabis oil help?
Research is still ongoing in this area, however some believe that due to its anti-inflammatory properties, CBD oil could possibly help reduce inflammation in those living with cystic fibrosis. It is not currently recommended by the CF Trust nor CF care teams.

4. Lungs, and other organs

Will he have other developmental or health issues?
There is nothing to suggest that a child with CF will be more predisposed to mental or learning difficulties.
Health issues are varied, however. CF is not just a lung condition. It affects many organs and causes a myriad of complications within the workings of the body.

- **Lungs**: A range of infections and reduced lung function, which impacts their health and wellbeing.

- **Liver**: The small ducts in the liver can become blocked due to problems with drainage of the bile out of the liver, causing liver disease. About 40% of those with CF will experience liver abnormalities, yet 8% will go on to develop CF-related liver disease.

- **Digestive system**: Many people with CF are pancreas insufficient, and some may require insulin with meals due to CF-related diabetes.

- **CF-related diabetes**: Inflammation and scarring of the pancreas can prevent effective production of insulin, leading to CF-related diabetes (CFRD). It affects about one third of adults, and 30% of children with CF.

- **Bones**: Those with CF may experience thinner and weaker bones at a younger age due to low bone mineral density, making them more fragile and likely to fracture. Around one-third of adults with CF have low bone mineral density.

- **Fertility**: Both men and women with CF could experience fertility issues. Most men (98%) will be infertile as the tube that carries the sperm to the testicles is either missing or blocked. They are not impotent; the sperm is healthy and fertile and they can father a child with IVF support. Similarly, women produce healthy, fertile eggs, but they might suffer irregular periods or thicker vaginal mucus, making conception trickier.

- **Cancer**: People with CF living so much longer is a hugely positive milestone, however it brings with it new concerns and research requirements. Although still not yet conclusive, recent research suggests those with CF might be more at risk of bowel cancer, but the reasons for this are still being studied.

- **Kidney and hearing complications**: Taking substantial amounts of antibiotics to help ward off infections, could cause toxicity in the kidneys and hearing.

- **Sinusitis**: Acute and chronic sinusitis are caused by the thick, sticky mucus building up in the sinuses. This can cause facial pain, congestion, loss of smell or taste, headaches and coughing.

- **Nasal polyps**: These tissue growths develop inside the nasal passage and sinuses as a result of chronic infection and congestion. Nasal polyps vary in size, and large ones will cause a blocked or runny nose, with a loss of smell or taste.

- **Clubbed fingers**: This is swelling in the fingers, which cause the finger nail to become rounder, known as 'nail clubbing'. The cause is unknown.

- **Sweat**: The sweat of people with CF contains very high levels of salt, which can crystallise on their skin and you can taste when you kiss someone with CF. This is why a sweat test is used to diagnose CF.

- **Meconium ileus**: When newborn babies are unable to pass their meconium (a baby's first stool), causing constipation and swelling of the tummy, and often resulting in surgery.[49]

Why does he get thick mucus in the lungs and what does it do to the lungs?

Small hair-like structures called cilia, push dust, germs and mucus out of the lungs, to be coughed out. Normally, a thin layer of slippery mucus helps everything move smoothly and easily along so the dirt and bacteria exit the lungs, protecting against infection.

However, in people with CF, the gene that controls the movement of salt and water in and out of cells is faulty. This makes the mucus that lines the airways and other organs thick and sticky, which prevents the cilia from performing their cleaning role effectively. The mucus clogs the lungs and bacteria grows, causing infections.

---

[49] All facts and figures sourced from the CF Trust website.

Frequent coughing and wheezing is common to try to clear the lungs of the thick mucus (sputum). Lung infections are treated with antibiotics as the lungs often aren't able to clear the bacteria without medical assistance. Over time, lung function decreases, due to lung damage from infections, as well as thickening of the walls of the airways, narrowing the lumens (the space inside the airways) and damage and obstruction to the airways. Eventually, lung function reduces so much that it can become life threatening.[50]

Why is he more prone to infection and what type of infection do you mean?

People living with CF are vulnerable to lung infections, or bugs, which can be picked up from the environment, as well as direct or indirect contact with other people with the condition or carrying the bacteria.

While these bugs are usually harmless to people who don't have CF, they can settle in the lungs and cause permanent lung damage for those living with CF. The thicker mucus makes it much more difficult for them to expel the bacteria, compared to those who don't have CF, which is why antibiotic help is often required.

Lung infections in those living with CF can be so serious that they can spend weeks in hospital on IV antibiotics. Infections can cause lung function to drop far lower than would be seen in someone with fully functioning lungs.

Common CF-related bugs include Pseudomonas, M. abscessus, B. cepacia and Aspergillus.

Pseudomonas is the most common lung infection in people with CF over the age of 16.[51] It is acquired from the environment and can sometimes be cleared or managed with antibiotic treatment. However sometimes it can become resistant to antibiotics, which can cause problems.

Due to the increased risk of infections, people with CF should not meet each other face-to-face for fear they may cross-infect types of bacteria that would be dangerous to each other.

---

[50] CF Trust website, 'Lungs and Cystic Fibrosis', https://www.cysticfibrosis.org.uk/what-is-cystic-fibrosis/how-does-cystic-fibrosis-affect-the-body/cystic-fibrosis-complications/lungs
[51] CF Trust website, 'Cystic fibrosis bugs', https://www.cysticfibrosis.org.uk/what-is-cystic-fibrosis/how-does-cystic-fibrosis-affect-the-body/symptoms-of-cystic-fibrosis/lungs/bugs

People with CF are more likely to pick up strains of Pseudomonas from each other, which can be harder to treat, which is just one reason why CF clinics keep people separate according to whether or not they have Pseudomonas.

According to the 2020 UK CF Registry, 32% of people with CF are living with chronic Pseudomonas.

What do I look for when checking for lung infections?

A key indicator of a lung infection is increased coughing and wheezing, getting out of breath and more sputum.

Once lung function reduces, can it be regained?

Lung function can drop significantly when an infection is present. This can return once the infection is treated with antibiotics.

Long term, as lung function deteriorates, this damage is permanent.

Infections are one of the main causes of lung damage, however there are many other reasons the lungs can deteriorate. The reason for the lung damage will determine if lung function can be regained, but in most cases a drop in lung function can be corrected back to baseline, or very close to it.

People taking the latest treatment Kaftrio, are reporting increased lung functions after a while of being on this wonder drug.

If he doesn't get frequent infections, will he still get lung damage?

Although infections are the main cause of lung damage, chronic inflammation can also be damaging, but to a lesser degree.

Do all CF people have lung infections?

It would be very uncommon for someone with CF to *never* get a lung infection, but how regularly and to what severity will vary from one person to the next.

At what lung function point would you resort to a lung transplant?

A double lung transplant is a possibility for those living with CF. Sometimes existing treatments no longer have an impact, and the lungs are so damaged that a transplant is the only option.

A lung transplant is based on a number of factors, but is often required when the lung function goes below 30%. Discussions about a referral to a transplant team for assessment would begin when the person's lung function is consistently below 40%. Paediatric CF centres of course would not likely have young patients at this lung function range, but more so in the older age groups.

Interestingly, although the transplant does not cure CF, the new lungs will not have CF. This is because the new lung cells from the donor who did not have CF would produce the CFTR protein that does not function in CF cells. The main issues experienced with transplants however, is rejection and infections due to being immunocompromised.

Transplants of other organs, including the liver, are also sometimes necessary due to the damage CF causes across the body's other organs.

Can I buy a machine to check his lungs?

When the child is able to complete the manoeuvres required for lung function testing, they will be provided a home lung function kit to use when requested by their CF team. This tends to be around four or five years old, approximately.

Every CF centre will differ, however, as it does depend on funding.

How successful is meconium ileus at being flushed through? Is the fact it didn't work a sign he has a bad case of CF? Why was the meconium ileus so bad?

About 20% of patients diagnosed with cystic fibrosis present with meconium ileus.[52] Of the patients with meconium ileus, around 95% will go on to be diagnosed with CF.

Signs of meconium ileus include a swollen tummy, green vomit and little or no passing of meconium.

Whether they can flush the meconium through without surgery, or they resort to an operation to create a stoma due to risk of the bowel perforating, neither are indicative of the severity of the CF.

---

[52] Meghana Sathe and Roderick Houwen, 'Meconium ileus in cystic fibrosis', *Journal of Cystic Fibrosis*, volume 16, supplement 2, November 2017

Apparently he can get free IVF on the NHS. Is this just his first child or as many rounds for as many children as he so wishes?

This will depend on the commissioning policies of the NHS when and where your child decides to start a family.

While cystic fibrosis does qualify for funding, it seems to vary heavily between countries and even areas, and there are also criteria their partner has to meet.

For those in England, you can consult your Clinical Commissioning Group for your area's specific criteria base. At the time of writing this in 2022 and according to the very useful CF Trust *Starting a Family* pack, in Wales and Scotland, those who meet the standardised criteria are eligible to two cycles of funded IVF. In N. Ireland, eligible parties can access one cycle of IVF and a frozen embryo transfer.

IVF can be a lengthy process and can cost around £5,000, but sometimes more, so funding for those with CF who wish to become parents is hugely important.

Will he have asthma?

It is common for someone with CF to develop asthma, as well as other respiratory conditions.

Due to the presence of CF however, it can be difficult to differentiate between asthma, and asthma-like symptoms caused by CF lung inflammation. The care team can look at family history to help them, and also the recurrence of wheezing episodes.

It is important that asthma is treated to help maintain normal lung function and minimise any symptoms such as cough or wheeze that are not due to infection.

Why do some get CF-related diabetes?

Most people with CF are pancreas insufficient, which means that the enzymes are unable to reach the digestive system to absorb food. It also causes inflammation and scarring of the pancreas, which can prevent effective insulin production, resulting in CF-related diabetes (CFRD) in both children and adults.

Data from the UK CF Registry 2020 indicates that more than one third of people with CF aged 16 and over are being treated for CFRD. For children aged 10–15 the percentage on treatment is 10%.

CFRD is different from Type 1 and Type 2 diabetes, but will still usually be treated with insulin. It is often picked up before symptoms occur via blood glucose monitoring.

5. Practical, everyday questions

Am I allowed to kiss him on the lips?

OK, so I know we shouldn't kiss newborn babies on the lips, but I meant at all. At any age. Ever. Thankfully, the answer is yes, you can kiss your child on the lips, and it's magical.

Of course, anyone with a cough, cold or any illness should avoid kissing on the lips to avoid germs being spread.

How do I differentiate between a common cough/cold and a cough that requires treatment?

Well isn't that the million-dollar question. Quite simply, there is no easy way of telling, which is why a cough swab is the answer. This long cotton bud-like swab tickles the back of the throat to make the child cough, and they then use this to see if any bacteria grows over the next few days. The swab will either come back clear, or it will help determine a specific bacteria and suitable antibiotic.

Generally speaking though, a wet, chesty cough is the sound of a possible CF-related infection, along with a possible snotty nose, raised temperature and generally being unwell.

That said, every time Bailey's swab has come back with an infection, he has been well and asymptomatic. Not only does this then hit you a bit harder as it's so unexpected, but it also shows there's no definite way of knowing.

What's the difference between a virus and bacteria?

Bacteria are living cells that can survive inside or outside the body. Viruses are a non-living collection of molecules that require a host to survive.

There are good bacteria, and there are some beneficial viruses too. Yet of course there are some bad ones, and many CF harmful bacteria live in stagnant water and mud.

Bacterial infections are very contagious, and can be caught when in close contact with someone (hugging or kissing), body fluids (sexual contact, coughs and sneezes) and touching surfaces contaminated with bacteria (for example, touching a door handle and then touching your nose or mouth). Bacterial infections might include a sore throat, ear infection or pneumonia.

When someone living with cystic fibrosis has a bacterial infection, they will often receive targeted antibiotics to kill it and clear the infection.

However, often viruses are left untreated. Viruses include measles, chickenpox and flu.

A common cold is a virus, but when your body is hard at work fighting off a virus, your immune system is weaker, so you're more susceptible to bacterial infections.

Can he wait in a doctors waiting room?

It's not advised to wait in a doctors waiting room due to the increased risk of catching any germs that other people might be carrying. This applies to waiting areas in hospitals and of course, CF clinics.

If you mention your child has CF, they will usually understandingly place you in a private room. Our GP usually put Bailey at the end of their list on his vaccination days so there was nobody else waiting to go in, which worked well. Always communicate with your GP about your child's condition and needs.

What if something happens to Bailey when I'm not at GOSH?

Often when we've had long hospital stays, the medical team become a bit of a safety net for us. That's how I felt, anyway.

People living with CF have a specialised care team, and you can always reach out to them with anything you need. Make sure you have their number in your Favourites on your phone so you can speed dial any time you want to give them a call.

What do I do with all his medicines when we fly somewhere?

Travelling abroad takes some careful planning and organisation. Packing enough meds, Creon and physio equipment for both the flight and the entire trip are all things to consider, as is getting it all through customs.

Be sure to pack enough Creon in your hand luggage for any food on the flight, as well as any meds you might need to take depending on the length of your journey. Your CF care team can provide a letter to list all your required medicines to enable you to get all the required drugs through customs on either end of your flight.

Always pack more than you need in case of loss or spillage, and if some medication needs to be kept in the fridge, take it on board in a cool bag.

Air conditioning on the flight can cause dehydration so your child must drink plenty of water and replenish salt levels. Similarly, hot climates can cause dehydration and sweating, so be sure they hydrate and top up sodium levels more than usual if you're going somewhere warm. If your child will require a nebuliser, ensure you have the right plug adapter for your destination country and make sure the battery is fully charged if you need to use it while on the flight. Keep in mind that if you're going somewhere hot, some antibiotics can make skin sensitive to the sun.

Will he still be able to get health insurance?

Yes, those with CF can get health insurance – the company will simply take into account their condition and adjust the terms and rates accordingly. The CF Trust are a great source of advice on this, so do reach out for their guidance.

Will he be able to get travel insurance?

It's essential that people living with cystic fibrosis have travel insurance in case they require medical assistance while away. Finding fairly-priced travel insurance can be quite difficult, and some insurance companies won't cover people with CF at all, so you'll need to check the company does cover this condition before booking.

If travelling as a family, it's recommended that the whole party be insured under the same policy as the person with cystic fibrosis. This means everyone's costs are covered if the trip is cancelled due to the person with CF falling unwell, plus it's only one number to call if an emergency arises.

Insurance policies within package holidays and school trips might not cover CF, so it's important to check with the agent or school provider.

Can he go to the pub for a pint of beer with Kev, Harry and Mylo when he is older?

Thankfully the answer is yes, people with CF can enjoy the odd tipple when old enough.

It's worth noting though that some people living with cystic fibrosis develop CF-related liver disease. Alcohol puts further stress on the liver, so excessive drinking wouldn't be recommended.

Like everything with CF it's getting that balance between living life, while being cautious and keeping your health and wellbeing in mind.

He needs a high-fat diet with additional salt, but how do I do this without impacting Harry and Mylo's healthy diet?
People living with CF require a high-fat diet due to some malabsorption in the digestive system, and need increased salt due to high salt losses.

On the whole, our three boys eat the same, but I sometimes add a sprinkle of salt to Bailey's food before I bring it to the table. If our meals include quite salty foods, such as sausages or some stock or gravy, then I don't add additional salt (unless it's particularly hot, or we're abroad).

The boys don't mind Bailey having extra salt, and we simply explained he needs it because he loses more salt due to his CF. It's so amazing how resilient, accepting and adjustable children are; far more so than adults.

In terms of fat, we give Bailey a lot of nuts, nut butters, hummus and avocado, but then the older two boys eat those too, so it's not hugely different.

If he loses salt, does he get thirstier?
Yes, you will find your little one wants and needs more water than usual. Not excessively, but due to the high salt loss, they need to replenish both fluid and electrolytes.

We leave a bottle of water in bed with Bailey, and his water bottle downstairs is always available on the kitchen table to have some when he wants. Yet again, this is the same for all the boys.

Do you wean babies with CF differently?
We weaned Bailey exactly as we did Harry and Mylo, however we did it slightly earlier on the advice of his dietician. We also probably focused more on getting in all the good fats to help his growth and weight gain, but then all babies need fat.

Work closely with the dietician within your CF care team and as always, take the lead from your child.

Will my big boys become more prone to infection too?
No, siblings cannot pick up CF, nor can the bacteria that are harmful to those with CF become harmful to children without the condition.

Can he have Calpol?
Yes, babies with CF can have Calpol, and no, Creon is not required.

Is the stoma the cause of the high output, or is the CF? Or both?
In Bailey's case, it was both. The stoma was very high up his ileum and he is totally pancreas insufficient, so everything was gushing out as quickly as it went in. It was like a perfect storm.

For some babies who have a stoma, it might be created lower down the digestive tract giving more time for absorption, or they perhaps might not be pancreas insufficient. They therefore then might have less of an output via their stoma.

Who cares for him once he is 16 and over?
Bailey is under the CF care team at Great Ormond Street Hospital. This is a children's hospital, so he will be with them until 16 to 18 years old, at which point he will be transferred to an adult hospital, such as the Royal Brompton.

Depending which CF care team your child is with, they should be able to confirm where they will be cared for as an adult if it's different to when they're a child.

Can he be with other babies? Can he go to play groups?
Yes, babies with CF can enjoy the company of other children, and indeed they should be around them to help them thrive, develop and learn to interact with their peers.

If you are attending a baby class and you wish to be sat slightly distanced from the group to avoid possible spread of germs, then explain your situation to the leader and they're sure to understand your request.

Should you notice another child with a cough or cold, discreetly choose a place furthest from them and try to avoid your child getting too close.

Can he go to nursery at all? If so, how will they know about his Creon?
Yes, babies with CF can attend nursery, and your CF care team will visit the nursery before they start to help educate the staff about cystic fibrosis, Creon doses and their need for a clean environment.

We felt apprehensive at first, obviously because of the potential spread of germs, but also entrusting someone else with Bailey's Creon. However, we knew deep down he needed the social interaction with children his own age and we believed it would help build up his immune system ready for school. We did instruct the nursery that he wasn't allowed to play with the mud kitchen or sandpit. We had the most amazing experience with Bailey's nursery, who were fully supportive of his needs and embraced their new way of doing things.

Can we have pets? We have a cat. Can we keep her?

Some people avoid having pets due to potential spread of germs and the fur potentially causing breathing issues. In contrast, there are many people living with CF who have dogs and cats as their loyal friends at home, often boosting their mood and reducing stress.

Research into the effects of pets on those living with CF showed increased nasal polyps for cat owners and greater wheezing in those who own both a cat and dog.[53]

It is recommended the animals do not sleep in children's cots or beds.

Sadly, our cat no longer lives with us, but this is our choice; we had to feel comfortable, so you do what is right for you and your family.

Must the boys wash their hands all the time now? Shall I wash my hands every time before I pick him up?

Handwashing and sanitising is very important in CF life, for both the person with CF themselves and those around them to help minimise the spread of bacteria through touch points. Consequently, cleaning is also paramount, so refer to chapter 6 for more information on that.

It's a fine balance between being extra vigilant and not making a child (or yourself) obsess over it. When we first came home from GOSH, I washed my hands so much that my skin was raw and bleeding. I was adamant I must still use anti-bacterial gel on my hands and it would sting so much that my eyes watered.

Of course, over time I realised I had gone overboard and now have a healthy balance, but antibacterial hand wash and hand gel are in great abundance in our cupboards, I do admit.

---

[53] Morrow, C. B., Raraigh, K. et al. 'Cat and dog exposure and respiratory morbidities in cystic fibrosis', *The Journal of Pediatrics*, 165(4), 830–5.e2, October 2014.

All the boys always wash their hands when coming home from school or sports, and when they come in from the garden. And we return them to the bathroom every time they 'forget' to wash their hands after going to the toilet. It's basic hygiene, just with a slight emphasis and heightened importance.

Should Kev shower when he gets home from rugby before picking up Bailey?

Kev works in a sweaty gym most days while training the rugby team. These environments are known to be breeding grounds for bacteria, in particular Pseudomonas. At first, when Bailey was so young, we did decide that Kev would shower and change his clothes when he returned home.

The actual answer from Bailey's CF care team was that a good hand wash upon his return would suffice, but we didn't feel comfortable with this, so we chose our own path. Now Bailey is a bit older and we are all a bit more familiar with things, Kev just washes his hands and changes his t-shirt.

You do what's right for you. If your partner is working in a small, quiet office all day, then maybe you won't feel it necessary. A hot, sticky, rarely-cleaned gym for a work location was just too much of a risk for us.

6. Emotional thoughts and worries

Why do I find this so catastrophic?

Who wouldn't, my dear? You've just been told that your darling innocent child has a condition that will hinder their health, need constant daily treatment and possibly cut short their life.

Give yourself grace. The most heart-breaking news in the world is that there is something wrong with your beloved little one. You want to do all you can to protect them, and here you are utterly helpless to do that very thing. This is huge. Any diagnosis is huge, CF or otherwise. You find this catastrophic simply because it is.

However, please hear me when I say this; it will get better. This dark place you find yourself in, will go from black to grey, and get paler as time wears on. I don't know yet if it ever goes, but I've accepted that it won't. It just gets lighter, and in a CF world that currently has so much hope, I believe it will get brighter still as we adjust and progress.

What feels so daunting and overwhelming now, will become more 'normal'. You will grow in confidence as you learn about CF and how to be a parent to a child with CF. You will become familiar with clinics, meds and physio, and you will find a lifestyle that is your normal. I know you don't want this to become your normal, but here you are, and you will find the strength and courage to accept all that it entails, purely for the sheer love of your child.

Is my reaction normal?

What's normal? How we each respond to any devastating news is so different. I've no doubt that specialists who bear the sad news of a CF diagnosis have seen it all and, in my opinion, almost feel like intruders on such a private moment simply by being present and witnessing parents' demise.

Any reaction to any diagnosis is normal – expressing our emotions in the rawest form is the most natural and healing way to handle the situation. Bottling it all up won't serve you. Let your pain, anguish and heartbreak seep out of you, and allow your head and heart to start their new journey forwards.

Do you think I am irresponsible for not knowing?

One in 25 people unknowingly walk around carrying the CF gene. How can anyone possibly know their invisible genetic makeup, unless we all have a genetic test? Carrying out genetic tests for millions of people simply isn't viable.

When a couple both have brown eyes, but their baby is born with blue eyes, this means they unknowingly carry the blue eye recessive gene. But how could they be expected to know that, given they have brown eyes?

It's the same with CF; it's a recessive gene and people can live healthy lives as genetic carriers, so it's little wonder so few of us know we carry the faulty gene.

If someone in your family has cystic fibrosis, you're entitled to receive a genetic test to check if you carry the gene, so you can make informed decisions when you wish to have your own family. If you are a carrier, but your partner does not carry the recessive gene, then you cannot give birth to a child with CF.

Was there anything I did while pregnant to cause this?

No mumma, there is nothing you did or didn't do while carrying your baby that gave them cystic fibrosis. I know you will think it, but please free yourself from the thought now as it is not serving you and is not accurate. It plagued me for months, and I don't want it to leave you in the same state.

Just like you couldn't control the colour of your child's eyes, you couldn't control whether or not they picked up the faulty CF genes. No amount of rest, healthy eating, knowing you were pregnant sooner so you didn't have that drink, or more/less exercise would have made any difference.

Whatever you feel you could or should have done differently, you are wrong. This was out of your control. It's both liberating and frustrating, I know, but that is the truth.

I can't get away from my guilt. Please help me!

Guilt envelopes you when you learn your baby has CF – or any condition or ailment, I'm sure. It's the most natural yet debilitating emotion out there, which is why I felt compelled to dedicate a standalone chapter to it. Head over to chapter 2 to read more, if you haven't already.

He will be so cross with us when he is older and understands what CF means for him. How do I tell him about CF?
In truth, I'm only just discovering the answers to this one myself now. Bailey is beginning to ask questions and some of them simply make my heart break into a million tiny pieces.

"But Harry and Mylo don't have to take Creon," Bailey said while trying to learn to swallow his new big boy Creon capsules aged two and half years old.

My eyes welled and my mind raced for a satisfactory, child-like explanation, but I fell short. I'm ashamed to say I almost brushed it aside, unable to talk for the lump in my throat. I swore to myself I would never do anything like that again, and so I armed myself with an acceptable response for the next time. This is how it went ...

"You need Creon to help you grow into a big, strong boy like your brothers. Harry and Mylo don't need to take it because they don't have cystic fibrosis like you. You need Creon so your tummy absorbs all the goodness from your yummy food."

Bailey now loves taking his Creon as he wants to be a big boy – as big as his brothers.

Cystic fibrosis is a learning curve each and every day. There's no end to it and the journey is always evolving. You adapt and grow with it as your child works through the ages and stages. The challenges and questions will change as your child does, and you need to move with them, swiftly, confidently and tenderly.

I am acutely aware that far more questions are coming, and I am ready to receive them. I learnt to always be prepared with a headful of answers that are respectfully honest, yet don't overwhelm.

Your CF care team will be able to give you advice on how to answer some of your child's questions as they begin to grow up, so always reach out for their support and guidance. You're not expected to know everything or have all the answers. Just like all parents, you're learning on the job, and being a parent to a child with cystic fibrosis is an even steeper learning curve.

How do I tell them?
One key lesson I learnt during CBT is not to make things into a big deal. Don't do the whole, 'sit down, I need to tell you something' scenario. This

will catastrophise the event and news. The best way is to gently and casually drip feed information throughout day-to-day life.

This is what we have done with both our bigger boys with all their questions, and something we are starting to do with Bailey. Hopefully this way, they will never remember a day they didn't know about CF – they just know.

Harry and Mylo are so good with Bailey, reminding him to take his Creon and steering him clear of stagnant water. Their acceptance is something I envy.

What if Bailey resents his brothers for not having CF?

This is still a question that consumes my thoughts, especially as Bailey grows older and is noticing points of difference, such as the fact they don't take Creon or have to do physio.

I wonder if there will be a time when Bailey is so annoyed he has this condition, that he does perhaps resent his brothers that it was him and not them. Knowing Bailey's nature as I do though, and seeing them together in their pack, I also wonder if he will brush the thought aside and feel thankful it wasn't his big boys.

Goodness, in truth I don't know. If I look to fellow CF people I've met virtually along the way, one lady's sister once said in an interview that she wishes she had CF and not her sibling. So maybe that's it; when you love someone, be that child, sibling or partner, you wish you could take away their condition and shoulder the burden.

How will Bailey ever forgive us?

Forgive is defined in the dictionary as, "to stop feeling angry or resentful towards someone for an offence, flaw or mistake".

As parents who carry the CF gene, what is our offence, flaw or mistake? Was it inheriting the gene at conception? Or perhaps passing on that gene? Well no to both, given we can't control either of those. Maybe you didn't know the gene was in your family heritage, in which case how could you have known to check if you're a CF gene carrier?

That's not to say this question still doesn't break my heart. It plagues me more than the previous question, actually. When my emotions get the better of me, or we're having a challenging CF day, I wallow in this thought.

In my rational, strong mind however, I can reason that yes, Bailey will likely feel angry, and rightly so, and in that anger he will lash out and blame those closest to him – his mummy and daddy. That's what all children do for all manner of things in life that feel unfair, unjust and damn right frustrating. As parents it's our responsibility to hear their hurt, feel their pain, listen to their frustrations, take on board their thoughts and simply be there. Don't defend, don't justify and don't answer back. Listen, feel and sit with them. When they're ready, and when they realise how this whole genetic thing works, they'll realise it's no more your fault that they have CF, than it is your parents' fault that you carry the gene.

At least, this is going to be my inexperienced approach. Aren't we all just winging it though, like every other parent?

They were all the questions I had, and I hope it answers some of yours, too. I have no doubt you will have so many other queries and concerns, but know that there is a wealth of support available to you.

The CF Trust website is always a great place to start, offering reliable and comprehensive advice. Always lean on your child's CF care team and ask them anything you need, no matter how silly it might seem.

CF children cannot be together, so it's not common for fellow parents to meet, however I know some that have. There's a whole community out there you can tap into should you wish, and when you feel ready. Forums, social media, websites, studies; take or leave whatever helps you through this time. Everyone is different, so just follow your own path and see what supports you.

ACKNOWLEDGEMENTS

With endless gratitude to Kev and my boys for putting up with my many late nights and weekends working on my passion project, and for ultimately pushing me over the finish line and letting me borrow your belief in me when doubt crept in.

Also huge thanks to The Group of Seven for bringing the cover design to life so personally, and to Philippa Payne for editing and proofreading my reams of copy.

A heartfelt thank you to those who contributed to make this book all that it is, including Lisa Du Plessis, Caroline Jordan and Liana Gomes. So grateful to you for adding so much value for our readers.

To all my family and friends, this is where I thank you for the love, support and kindness when Bailey was born, and again now for being such cheerleaders of this book.

And finally to you, the person reading this. Thank you for believing in this book enough to pick it up and read it. If you are on a journey with your child, I hope that it serves you well, and that it offers the comfort and knowledge you long for, and so deserve.

ABOUT THE AUTHOR

Laura's love of the written word began while studying English Literature at Royal Holloway, University of London. She went on to become a successful copywriter and content editor for a number of consumer brands, magazines and websites. Today she uses her writing skills to fulfil her purpose of supporting other parents and helping raise awareness of cystic fibrosis through her book and several national newspaper articles.

A keen runner, vegetarian, DIY lover and constant Earl Grey tea drinker, Laura is often found on the sidelines of a football or rugby pitch cheering on one of her three boys or husband. Settled in her small, rural Hertfordshire village in England, Laura loves nothing more than gardening in the summer and cosying up by the fire with her tribe of boys in the winter.

Image credit: Kay Young Photography

Printed in Great Britain
by Amazon